WANT :- POLICEMAN £20
- (BRIDESMAID £20)
- MOTHER 1999
- EASTER GREETINGS   - SYDNEY £65

- RAINY DAY £20-30
- FATHER £30
- Statue of liberty
- Detective

Bunnykins and Beatrix Potter
Price Guide

ROYAL DOULTON • BESWICK • ROYAL ALBERT

HAVE :-
ANGEL (£30)
SAILOR (Prussia)
MOTHERS - DAY £18
HALLOW'EEN £22
JUDGE (Joining piece)
FIREMAN (BLUE) £18
FIREMAN (RED) £80
SWEETHEART (Prussia)
UNCLE SAM (XMAS)
JOCKEY (£68)
UK case

FISHERMAN (£25)
AIRMAN £70 (21st B.Day)
BUSINESSMAN £70
MYSTIC (Xmas)
COWBOY (21st B.Day)
INDIAN (21st B.Day)
SIGHTSEER £35
ASTRO £85
TOURIST £35
SUNDIAL £30
ORDERED
SANTA'S helper (colourway) £70 Prussia
FORTUNE Teller £35
MORRIS DANCER £35

Francis Joseph Publications
ISBN 1 870703 13 8

Acknowledgements

I would like to thank all the contributors to this book, without whom it would not have been possible. I would like to make special mention of Sir John Bartlett who died in the summer of 1998. He provided the Beatrix Potter items for the photograph section. Also Harvey May who pulled out all the stops for me on the Beatrix Potter listings, Catherine Braithwaite for her section on Series Ware, Doug Pinchin for his text and refinement of certain errors.

Malcolm and Jennifer Hutchinson provided the pieces for the Bunnykins section, and Nick Tzimas provided the price guide. The photography is by Trevor Leek, and the typesetting and layout by John Folkard.

F J Salmon

© Francis Joseph Publications 1998

Second edition

Published in the UK by
Francis Joseph Publications
5 Southbrook Mews, London SE12 8LG

Typeset and printed, in Great Britain by
E J Folkard Print Services
199 Station Road, Crayford, Kent DA1 3QF

ISBN 1 870703 13 8

Contents

Charles Noke's simple Bunnykins designs were the beginning of the whole Bunnykins collecting phenomenon.

Introduction: The Rise and Rise of Bunnykins and Beatrix Potter Figures

Bunnykins to the Fore

The collectables market is fickle but during the last twenty years or so the name of Royal Doulton has consistently ranked high in the collectability stakes. The enthusiasm for the myriad of ceramics produced by the company shows no sign of failing. Even within the world of collecting Royal Doulton fashions change. The causes of these changes are as difficult to define with Royal Doulton as with any other product. What is certain is that Royal Doulton items hold some special magic for collectors and while, say, character jugs may not be so popular this year their time will come again. Traditionally, figurines, character jugs, series ware and Lambeth pottery are the most popular Doulton collectables but in the past few years their pole position has been challenged. The challenge has come from an unexpected and hitherto comparatively neglected area of Royal Doulton's activity – Bunnykins figures.

For many years there have been collectors of Bunnykins tableware, however the cute little rabbits which initially evolved from the characters depicted on the plates and cups and saucers had been largely ignored by adult collectors. They had remained confined to the nursery. This was after all their intended destination. So what caused Bunnykins collectors to multiply like, well, rabbits? It is not easy to be certain what caused this surge of interest but there are a couple of factors which might have played a part. The first was the commissioning of the Bunnykins Collectors Band by UK Fairs Ltd. This was a colourway of the Bunnykins Oompah Band which was made in a limited number of 250 sets and only available at the UK Doulton Collectors Fair in October 1990. The edition was sold out on the day. The success of the Band caused considerable interest in the Doulton world. Collectors became Bunnykins aware. UK Fairs and its sister company, UK International Ceramics, spurred on by the strength of the somewhat unexpected interest in Bunnykins figures commissioned further limited editions. The Bunnykins Royal family in a new colourway came next followed by a range of new characters all in limited editions. Around the world special Bunnykins commissions for specific markets ensured that the Bunnykins figure phenomenon became international.

The other factor which may have fuelled the take-off of Bunnykins figures is the behaviour of Royal Doulton itself. Bunnykins figures in their present form were introduced in 1972. By 1974 there were still only fifteen models in the range and no more characters were added until 1982. Neither were there any withdrawals during this period. By 1985 the range had more than doubled. No doubt the 50th Anniversary celebrations of Bunnykins tableware in 1984 had helped things along. The pace of introductions quickened during the mid 1980s, but only a handful of models were discontinued. However in 1987-88 a significant number of figures were withdrawn, almost instantly transforming them into secondary market collectables.

The combination of 'special' Bunnykins figures becoming available and a number of 'standard' Bunnykins figures becoming unavailable may have caused the spark that ignited the market. It is impossible to be certain of the reasons but it is undeniable that Bunnykins figures together with Beatrix Potter figures have become two of the leading collectables of the 1990s.

The Beatrix Potter Figure Phenomenon

Unlike the Bunnykins Characters which were largely the brain-child of the ceramics industry, the Beswick Beatrix Potter figures have a much longer pedigree. It is just over one hundred years since Beatrix Potter wrote an illustrated letter to a sick child about the adventures of a rabbit called Peter and over ninety years since her original stories were first commercially published. Every generation since has fallen under the spell of her characters and their adventures. From 1948 enthusiasts could purchase ceramic models of Peter Rabbit and his friends produced by the Beswick pottery. The little figures, closely and accurately modelled on Beatrix Potter's drawings were an immediate success and have remained so ever since, surviving the takeover of Beswick by Royal Doulton in 1969 and the change of brand name to Royal Albert in 1989 and their subsequent return to the Beswick backstamp.

In recent years the already strong interest in the stories and characters of Beatrix Potter has grown to huge proportions. All manner of Beatrix Potter merchandise is now available. Everything from bed-linen to postage stamps has been produced featuring the familiar characters. The centenary of the first Peter Rabbit story in 1993 and the resulting promotional activity added to the public's awareness of Beatrix Potter's work. As could be expected, the popularity of the Beswick/Royal Albert figures also flourished. The demand for more information resulted in the publication of a flood of books, not only about Beatrix Potter and her stories but also about the figures. Initially a chapter in the *Beswick Collectors Handbook* by Harvey May listed, for the first time, all the Beswick Beatrix Potter figures and then five years later in 1992 *Beatrix Potter Figures* edited by Louise Irvine was devoted solely to the whys and wherefores of collecting the figures and their associated products. As so often happens with the publication of a specialised book, even more more collectors were brought into the market. Armed with new information the search was on for the elusive discontinued models as collectors strived to complete their collections.

How This Book Will Help You

It is indisputable that there are many similarities in the appeal of Royal Doulton Bunnykins figures and Beswick/Royal Albert Beatrix Potter figures. They may have sprung from a different area of inspiration but in today's collectables market they are inexorably linked. It is not unusual to find that collectors enthusiastically collect both ranges. The market for both continues to go from strength to strength. In addition to providing a complete listing of both ranges, (in alphabetical order) it is also the intention of this book to help collectors gain an insight into a sometimes bewildering aspect of collecting – pricing.

Each entry is given a price in the form of a range of values the collector might expect to pay for the figure on the open market. However the old maxim that something is only worth what someone is prepared to pay for it holds true but faced with an ever growing number of discontinued models it is helpful to have a guide to the general market value of a piece. In the final analysis the collector must decide if the asking price is acceptable to him. If the answer is 'yes' then that is the true value of the item.

Bunnykins and Beatrix Potter figures are no longer solely the province of young collectors. Adults and children alike have fallen under their enchantment. Could it be that we are really all still children at heart?

The Bunnykins Figure Story

It might be seen as improbable that the creator of Bunnykins was a nun. However, Barbara Vernon Bailey was a nun with connections. Her father was Cuthbert Bailey, the general manager of Royal Doulton's factory in Burslem, Stoke on Trent. It was he who saw the potential in the sketches of the rabbit family Sister Mary Barbara regularly sent home from the convent school where she taught. The rabbits bore a strong likeness to her own family, in particular Father Rabbit with his round spectacles and ever present pipe which reminded many of Cuthbert Bailey himself. He obviously did not mind the comparison as he had Barbara's drawings adapted for production on a range of Royal Doulton childrens china. The artist chosen to do this work was Hubert Light. Previously he had designed some of the early figures in Royal Doulton's HN range. His most enduring legacy to the Bunnykins collection is the familiar border of running rabbits which, albeit in a redrawn form, is still in use today. The new Bunnykins nurseryware was introduced in 1934 and at once proved successful. Gradually all other Royal Doulton nurseryware designs were withdrawn from production leaving Bunnykins to reign supreme. It consisted entirely of practical tableware pieces and apart from one or two additional items and various shape and body updates remains much the same.

The first decorative items were launched in 1939. These were the first Bunnykins figures, and were a family of rabbits, Farmer Bunnykin, Mother Bunnykin, and their four 'children', Billy, Reggie, Mary and Freddie. Royal Doulton promoted them, together with a bunny-shaped range of tableware, as part of the Bunnykins range. However the models have little in common with the Bunnykins family as portrayed on the nurseryware. These early figures, which are thought to have been designed by Royal Doulton's Art Director, Charles Noke, are more akin to some of the anthropomorphic figures in the HN range. Nevertheless they have always been considered as part of the Bunnykins collection and carried the Bunnykins backstamp. Interestingly they are usually marked Bunnykin rather than Bunnykin<u>s</u>. The production life of these figures was remarkably short as the outbreak of the 2nd World War ended the production of most decorative ceramic items. When production slowly resumed after 1945 some pre-war items were reintroduced including Bunnykins nurseryware but not the Bunnykins figures

The popularity of Bunnykins tableware continued to increase in the post-war years. Walter Hayward, who for some time had adapted Barbara Vernon's sketches for production took over as designer. Barbara Vernon's facsimile signature continued to be used for a while but Hayward's style was rather different and recognisable. The scenes have more rabbits in them and little mice take a more active part in the proceedings.

Bunnykins Figures Make a Comeback

It was not until the early 1970s that the idea of a range of complimentary Bunnykins figures was again considered. The acquisition of the Beswick factory by Royal Doulton in 1969 may have influenced the decision to relaunch Bunnykins figures. The factory specialised in animal models and for twenty years or so had enjoyed great success with their Beatrix Potter figures. It was from this pool of experience that the new Bunnykins figures emerged. Indeed the style and scale of the new range had much more in common with the Beswick figures than the original Bunnykins figures of 1939. In fact the designer of the first Beatrix Potter figures, Albert Hallam, was also the creator of the new Bunnykins figures.

With the wealth of ideas available from the tableware designs of Barbara Vernon and Walter Hayward it is not surprising that the first characters were directly lifted from nurseryware scenes. Between 1972 and 1974 fifteen models were introduced, all of them being taken directly from tableware designs. It is noticeable that the colour schemes used for the figures reflect the colourings of the original drawings.

After this initial burst of activity Royal Doulton seemed to loose interest in Bunnykins figures. No further figures were introduced for eight years but interestingly no figures were withdrawn either. This rather indicates that the company considered Bunnykins figures enough of a commercial success to remain in production but perhaps not quite successful enough to warrant too much promotional activity.

Bunnykins Figures Make a Comeback – Again

The renaissance of Bunnykins figures started for a second time in the early 1980s. Harry Sales had been appointed Design Manager of the Beswick factory in 1975. He was a great supporter of Bunnykins but saw that the potential for Bunnykins figures lay in a totally different direction to what had gone before. This is evident from the models which were introduced under his influence. The first of these introductions were a mixture of conventional style characters such as **Mr. Bunnykins at the Easter Parade** (DB18) and **Santa Bunnykins** (DB17) and the new approach which is illustrated by **Jogging Bunnykins** (DB22) and the sporting Bunnykins which followed

The new style figures pass a witty comment on human activities and frailties. The expression on the face of **Jogging Bunnykins** strikes a cord with anyone who has seen an overweight jogger of the human variety valiantly plodding along the road, and the supreme optimism of **Bogey Bunnykins** looking in vain for his golf ball which remains steadfastly at his feet can be seen on any golf course at any time. The new style characters represent a move to broaden the appeal of the figures from being purely aimed at children into the adult collectables market. The entire family could now enjoy collecting Bunnykins figures.The new figures were obviously not so closely tied to the nurseryware range and employed a brighter selection of colours to add extra appeal to their intended audience.

Customised Bunnykins Figures

The 50th anniversary of Bunnykins was celebrated in 1984. The **Bunnykins Oompah Band** was issued in that year and as part of the promotional activity **Drummer Bunnykins** (DB26) carried on his drum the legend '50th Anniversary'. After 1984 the drum is inscribed 'Bunnykins Oompah Band'. 1984 was also an Olympic year. The games were held in Australia and a colourway of **Olympic Bunnykins** in the Australian national colours of green and gold was produced for the Australian market. The two events were the first instances of Bunnykins figures being customised. There followed two colourways for special events in the United States and **Uncle Sam Bunnykins** (DB50) was produced for sale in the U.S.A. **Collector Bunnykins** (DB54) was commissioned in 1987 by the Royal Doulton International Collectors Club. It had been the practice of the club to commission special pieces from the various Royal Doulton ranges exclusively for their members. At this point in the club's history the items were only available for a limited period of time, usually about six months. Two of the most popular items had been 'Prized Possessions' and 'Pride and Joy', a pair of seated figures showing somewhat elderly collectors studying the relevant reference books on their collecting interest, Royal Doulton Figures and Royal Doulton Character Jugs respectively. As the Bunnykins Collectors Book had recently been published it was appropriate that **Collector**

Bunnykins should be shown in a similar pose. As this figure was only available for a very short time it is now considered one of the most difficult to find and consequently one of the most valuable. It is important as it played a vital part in awakening collectors interest in Bunnykins figures. It was also one of Harry Sales last Bunnykins designs as he left Royal Doulton in 1986.

Another Change of Direction

The next few years saw the increase in both withdrawals from production and the number of special commissions for Bunnykins figures. Bunnykins figure collecting started to come of age.

With the departure of Harry Sales the style of Bunnykins figures once again changed. Graham Tongue took over as Design Manager and consequently responsibility for the Bunnykins range. Under his guidance the subjects portrayed moved away from adult activities to which which were intended to have appeal to younger children while having a slight educational aspect to them. Others featured childrens activities such as scouting – **Be Prepared Bunnykins** (DB56), and guides – **Brownie Bunnykins** (DB61). It is also noticeable that the rabbits themselves undergo a slight change, the poses become more 'human'.

The Influence of Colin Twinn's Designs

Changes were also happening to the designs used on Bunnykins tableware and these were to have an influence on the figures. In 1987 it was decided to publish a series of childrens books using the Bunnykins characters. There had been other Bunnykins publications but on this occasion the publisher was to be Frederick Warne and Co. Ltd. who were best known as the publisher and copyright holder of the Beatrix Potter stories. Colin Twinn, a successful childrens book illustrator was brought in to develop the Bunnykins characters for publication. It was intended to use some of his designs on the nurseryware. The result of Mr. Twinns work was a completely new look for Bunnykins. A new Bunnykins family was created who lived in a softer coloured world of idealised rolling countryside. The rabbits again metamorphosed with larger ears and slightly stylised bodies. A great number of scenes were eventually issued on the tableware to a mixed reception from the public. Some of Colin Twinns designs are still in production but the majority were withdrawn after a few years. However the Bunnykins figure collection gained a number of new characters. Some of the older subjects were remodelled and renamed to fit in with Colin Twinn's new Bunnykins family, for example **Family Photograph** (DB1) became **Father**, **Mother** and **Victoria Bunnykins** (DB68), **Tally Ho** (DB12) became **William Bunnykins** (DB69) and **Busy Needles** (DB10) became **Susan Bunnykins** (DB70). New members of the family were designed by Graham Tongue based on Colin Twinn's illustrations, (**Polly Bunnykins** DB71, **Tom Bunnykins** DB72 and **Harry Bunnykins** DB73). In general most of the introductions of the late 1980s show the influence of Colin Twinn's redesigned Bunnykins illustrations.

Bunnykins Figures in the 1990s

The market for Bunnykins figures in the 1990s has been dominated by special commissions. The ground breaking **Bunnykins Collectors Band** (DB86-90) led the way for many similar limited editions. In Great Britain UK International Ceramics consolidated their position as the prime source of new Bunnykins commissions. In other markets there has been a mixture of private commissions, such as Magician Bunnykins (DB126) and commissions originating from Royal Doulton's overseas companies, notably Royal Doulton Australia with **Aussie Surfer**

Bunnykins (DB133) and Royal Doulton U.S.A. who have issued several colourways for promotional tours. The market for these special editions shows no sign of slowing down. Each new issue is greeted with enthusiasm by collectors, many of whom go to great lengths to obtain models not available in their home market.

Fifteen figures were withdrawn from production in 1993. Currently the collection consists of around twenty figures. At present it seems there will be more new models issued as special commissions than directly from Royal Doulton but this could easily change. What does not seem set for change however is the strength of the collectors market for Bunnykins figures.

The Bunnykins family are now set to become film stars. An animated film has been produced and sold to television stations around the world. It will eventually be made available to collectors in video form and the first public showing in Britain was at the UK Doulton Collectors Fair in October 1995. The popularity of Bunnykins figures is further enhanced by the fact that the Royal Doulton International Collectors Club in the USA produced a special double Bunnykins figure to celebrate the club's fifteenth birthday.

It would seem that it is not only **Surfer Bunnykins** who is riding the crest of the wave – the Bunnykins story just goes from strength to strength.

Bunnykins Series Ware

Bunnykins Series Ware was almost exclusively made for children's meal-times and as so, the shapes and material were often designed to withstand wear and tear. Both earthenware and bone china were made available. Aside from tea-sets, the initial productions of the 1930s range also included a range of night-lights and candleholders. Later, moneybanks, saving books, clocks and Christmas tree ornaments were added. The Series Ware falls into three main categories: Flatware, hollow ware and unusual moulded subjects.

A Bunnykins catalogue from the 1930s.

Flatware

In 1934, Cuthbert Bailey chose Hubert Light to adapt his daughter Barbara's drawings to feature on children's dinner, tea and breakfast ware. Collectors can easily identify these early illustrations because they bare the facsimile name 'Barbara Vernon'. The value of any piece from this period is generally higher, but not always, than those which were produced later.

Since flatware was made in quantity, one stands a good chance of finding such pieces at a boot fair or local auctions. Check the condition, since they were usually well-used and so the transfer is often scratched. A clean image bearing Barbara's signature on a 7-inch plate could fetch between £30/$50 and £40/£65. The value of an interesting subject like a 'Game of Golf' is two-fold. A golfing subject appeals to golf fanciers as well as Bunnykins collectors and therefore the value increases, hence £50/$80 to £60/$100. The Royal Doulton Museum in Stoke-on-Trent holds the pattern books which list the Series' title references and production dates. *The Golfer*, for instance, has the reference HW4R and was in production from 1937 until 1952, placing it firmly in the early desirable category.

The variety of wares produced broadened throughout the late 1930s and 1940s, withstanding the lull of the war years. Included in the range were cake-stands, fruit dishes, hot water and porridge plates, which feature a vast range of subjects designed by the ingenious hand of Barbara Vernon. The *Dog Carriage* (1937-1952) and *Chicken Pulling a Cart* (1940-1952) were two unusual examples from the period because they introduced animals (other than bunnies) as central characters.

In the 1950s, Barbara Vernon became more involved with her work at the convent and so, Walter Hayward took over the illustration designs. His designs are similar to Barbara's but do not normally bear her facsimile signature. Value is subsequently less for each piece averaging at £20-£25/$30-$40, even though some of his earliest designs were adapted from Barbara's and bear her signature.

Barbara Vernon's designs appear to have been in production for approximately 22 to 25 years, so you have a good chance of building a good collection of her work. Walter Hayward's designs were greeted more erratically – some lasting only three years (*Bonfire* LF128 and *Hoopla* LF129). These rare subjects are more valuable simply because less were made. Colin Twinn took over with his own style in 1987 incorporating more detail. Already a successful children's book illustrator, his designs were more naturalistic and less simplistic. Like all his predecessors, the trademark bunnies run round the edge of the design.

A Casino *shaped teapot produced c1939 featuring 'Medicine Time' designed by Barbara Vernon. Introduced in 1937 and withdrawn by 1952. Value: £400-£500/$660-$825.*

Hollow wares

Just as the adults of the 1930s demanded stylistic art deco shapes for their tables and mantelpieces, so the children's tea-sets followed suit. Shapes like *Casino*, a stepped geometric body was a popular choice of the late 1930s, but it is virtually impossible to find a complete Bunnykins tea-set in the shape and even if you are lucky, it could cost £1500/$2400 plus. A pot alone costs £450/$745, and a cup and saucer cost between £50-£75/$80-$125. This clashes with Doulton's intentions in the 1930s. The original advertisers sold on the following premise:

A Don shaped mug produced between 1937 and 1983 feauring 'Embracing at a Window', designed by Barbara Vernon (introduced in 1937, withdrawn by 1952). Value: £60-£80/ $100-$30.

> *A welcome fact is their inexpensiveness,*
> *a set will not cost you much*

The *Casino* shape lasted production from 1937 until 1968. The rounder, more traditional *Don* shape was used on mugs and beakers was produced from 1937 right up to 1983 and is therefore, more commonly seen. The *Albion* shape replaced *Casino* for teapots and jugs and *Stratford, Malvern, Rex,* and *Prince* shapes are also to be found.

What is nice, is that subject matter was often sensitively picked to match use. Both candleholders in these photographs suggest the time of day. They might be used to light the way to bed as in *Bedtime*

Two candleholders introduced in 1940 and withdrawn in 1952. Value £400-£600/$660-$990.

Two rare bunny teapots produced in the 1930s reflect the vogue for different and unusual shapes. The moulded bunny shaped on the right is part of a teaset by Charles Noke c1939. It is worth between £1000-£1500/$1650-$2475 on its own.

in *Bunks* (1937-1952) or to wait up for Father Christmas in *Santa Claus* (1940-1952).

Candleholders are extremely rare and appear on the market infrequently. Made between 1940 and 1952, they fetch anywhere from £400/$660 to £600/$990. Nightlights are just as rare and would command the same sort of purchasing price. A more reasonable collection to start with would be egg cups. Those by Barbara are either footed egg-cups or the *Don* shape and appear with her designs in 1937. They are:

EC1	Sleeping in a rocking chair
EC2	Drummer
EC3	Sheltering under an umbrella
EC4	Holding hat and coat
EC5	Trumpeter
EC6	Playing with cup and spoon
EC7	Raising hat

The egg-cup shape was changed in 1968 to a more squat shape..

Moulded Wares

These are often the rarest of all the three categories of wares. In fact a moulded rabbit egg-cup made c1939 recently sold at £1850 at auction. Even more staggering, a moulded bunny sugar-sifter fetched £7590 inclusive at John Bellman's of West Sussex in July 1997!

The new vogue for unusually shaped teapots in the

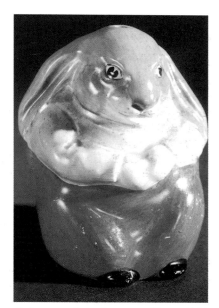

A bunny shaped sugar-sifter c1939 designed by Charles Noke. This made a staggering £7590/ $12,525 at auction. It was spotted by a couple of knowledgeable collectors with an unbelieveable pre-sale estimate of £20-£30/$35-$50.

1930s gave Doulton the idea to extend this to the bunny range. Indeed, you could purchase a whole set of bunny shaped tea ware including pot, milk and sugar.

Introduced in 1939 this range was short-lived and Charles Noke's design was withdrawn fairly quickly due to the Second World War and therefore was destined to become rare and extremely valuable. More information on the designs themselves and later additions to the range (current and otherwise) can be found in Lousie Irvine's *Royal Doulton Bunnykins* a collector's book published by Richard Dennis in 1993.

Charles Noke's bunny teaset circa 1939. From bottom left: milk jug and right sugar bowl (value: £2000/$3300 plus). Above this is the eggcup which made £2000/$3300 at auction. This was a rare find; the only other one which surfaced at auction made £1500/$2475 in spite of damage.

A range of 1980s boxed giftware.

Bunnykins Backstamps

The backstamps used on Royal Doulton Bunnykins figures have been modified several times since 1972. This is a result of changes in Royal Doultons exact trading title. However as it would seem that once a Bunnykins figure is issued it retains the backstamp current at the time of issue for its entire production life backstamps are of very little help in dating the figure. By identifying the backstamp it is possible to ascertain, within a few years, the introduction date of the character. The date found incorporated in the backstamp is the date the figure was copyrighted, not necessarily the date of introduction. Usually the copyright is obtained the year before a model is added to the range. This however is not a hard and fast rule as there are some instances where a figure has been copyrighted and issued within the same year.

A feature of the Bunnykins market are the numerous special commissions and limited edition colurways. This has led to a number of backstamp variations which give details of the commissioning organisation and can also include some extra information. For example, Collector Bunnykins has a backstamp which not only records its exclusivity to members of the Royal Doulton International Collectors Club but also gives the modellers name, an unusual departure for a Bunnykins backstamp. The first backstamp which defines the size of a limited edition is to be found on Drummer Bunnykins (DB89), part of the Bunnykins Collectors Band. Although the Collectors Band consists of five figures it is only the Drummer who has this amended backstamp. It is now usual for the edition size to be recorded where it is appropriate.

The first individually numbered backstamp is to be found on Rock and Roll Bunnykins (DB124) which was commissioned by Royal Doulton USA in a limited edition of 1000 to celebrate the opening of the Cleveland Rock and Roll Hall of Fame in 1991.

Unlike Beatrix Potter figures the value of a Bunnykins figure is not affected by its backstamp.

Illustrated are six representative Bunnykins Figure backstamps.

Listed are descriptions of the various backstamps found on Bunnykins figures that have been on general sale.

1   Royal Doulton Lion and Crown backstamp. Bunnykins in upper case type. Character or title in lower case with quotation marks. Royal Doulton Tableware Ltd. in upper case type. Copyright date and DB number included. 1972-84.
    There are two variations of this mark
    a Royal Doulton Tableware Ltd changed to Doulton and Co. Limited, and design registration numbers included. c1974.
    b For the 50th anniversary year of Bunnykins 'Golden Jubilee Celebrations' was added to the usual backstamp. Upper case type used. 1984.

2   Royal Doulton Lion and Crown backstamp. Character name or title in upper case type with quotation marks. Company name changed to Royal Dolton (UK). 1985-86.

3   Royal Doulton Lion and Crown backstamp. Title or character name in upper case type. (UK) dropped from company name. Used on all new models from 1977.

Special commissions and editions have an adapted Bunnykins backstamp and are self explanatory.

Backstamp used on the first Bunnykins figures issued in 1939. Note the use of Bunnykin in the singular.

Backstamp used on Bunnykins figures c1974.

Backstamp currently in use on all Bunnykins figures on general sale.

The first individually numbered limited edition backstamp used for Rock and Roll Bunnykins DB124.

Backstamp used on Bunnykins figures commissioned by UK International Ceramics Ltd.

Backstamp used on Collector Bunnykins which was commissioned by the Royal Doulton International Collectors Club for sale only to its members.

Ace Bunnykins, DB42, 1986, £120-£130 / $200-$215.

Aerobic Bunnykins, DB40, 1985-1988, £90-£100 / $150-$165.

Aussie Explorer Bunnykins Teapot, D7027, 1996, £60 / $100. Exclusive to John Sinclair Ltd Edition of 2500.

Astro Bunnykins Rocket Man, DB20, 1983-1988, £100-£120 / $165-$200.

Below: *Australian Bunnykins*, DB58, 1988, £650-£750 / $1080-$1240. Commissioned by Royal Doulton Australia to commemorate Australia's Bicentenary.

Aussie Surfer Bunnykins, DB133, 1994, £90-£100 / $150-$165. Commissioned by Royal Doulton Australia to celebrate 60 years of Bunnykins.

Ballerina Bunnykins, DB176, 1988, £20 / $35.

Banjo Player Bunnykins, DB182, 1998-Cur, £58 / $95.

Bathtime Bunnykins, DB148, 1994-1997, £20-£30 / $35-$50.

Batsman Bunnykins, DB144, 1994, £160-£180 / $265-$300. UKI Ceramics Exclusive. Limited Edition of 1000.

Be Prepared Bunnykins, DB56, 1987-1996, £20-£30 / $35-$50.

Bedtime Bunnykins, Left: DB79, 1988, £650-£750/$1080-$1240. Special Colourway for Bells USA. Right: DB63, 1987, £180-£200/$300-$330. Special colourway for DH Holmes USA.

Bedtime Bunnykins, (left) DB103, 1991, £110-£120/$180-$200. Special Colourway for Royal Doulton USA Collector Events, and (right) DB55, 1987-1996, £20/$35.

A selection of *Billie & Buntie Bunnykins Sleigh Ride*, Left: DB4, 1972-current, £20/$35; Top right: DB4, 1972, £20/$35. Example of colour variation; Bottom right: DB81, 1989, £160-£180/$265-$300. Special Colourway for Royal Doulton USA Collector Events.

Beefeater Bunnykins, DB163, 1996, £180-£200/$300-$330 UKI Ceramics Exclusive Limited Edition of 1500.

Billie Bunnykins Cooling Off, DB3,1972-1987, £200-£220/$330-$365.

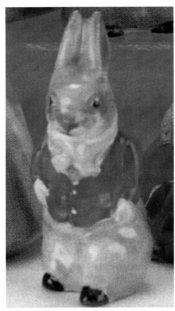

Billy Bunnykins, D6001, c1939-1940, £800-£1200/$1320-$1980.

Bogey Bunnikins, DB32, 1985-1992, £100-£120/$165-$200.

Bowler Bunnykins, DB145, 1994, £160-£180/$265-$300. UKI Ceramics Exclusive. Limited Edition of 1000.

Boy Skater Bunnykins, DB152, 1995-current, £20/$35

Bride Bunnykins, DB101, 1991-current, £20/$35.

Bridesmaid Bunnykins, DB173, 1997-current, £20/$35.

Brownie Bunnykins, DB61, 1987-1996, £60-£80/$100-$130.

Buntie Bunnykins Helping Mother, DB2, 1972-1997, £60-£80/$100-$130.

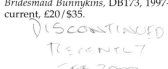

DISCONTINUED RECENTLY FEB 2000

Busy Needles, DB10, 1973-1988, £100-£120/$165-$200.

Carol Singer Bunnykins Music Box, DB53, 1986-1990, £150-£200/$250-$330.

Carol Singer Bunnykins, DB53, 1991, Limited Edition 1000, £200-£250/$330-$415. UKI Ceramics Exclusive.

City Gent Bunnykins Teapot, D6966, 1994, £75-£80/$125-$130. Exclusive to John Sinclair Limited Edition of 2500.

Cheerleader Bunnykins: Left: DB143. Yellow colourway sold at UK Royal Doulton Fairs only. Right DB142, Orange colourway. Both 1994, £80-£100/$130-$165 each. UKI Ceramics Exclusive. Limited Edition of 1000.

Cavalier Bunnykins, DB179, 1998, £180-£200/$300-$330.

Clarinet Player Bunnykins, DB184, 1998, £58/$95. UKI Ceramics exclusive, Limited Edition of 2500.

Clown Bunnykins, Left: DB129, 1992, £1200-£1500/$1980-$2475. Limited Edition of 250. Sold at 10th Park Lane Fair only. Right: DB128, 1992, £650-£750/$1080-$1240, Limited Edition of 750. Both UKI Ceramics Exclusive.

Collector Bunnykins, DB54, 1987, £600-£650/$990-$1080, RDICC Exclusive.

Constable Mountie Bunnykins. DB135 from Lambeth Prod., 1993, £650-£750/$1080-$1240.

Daisie Bunnykins Springtime, DB7, 1972-1983, £300-£350/ $495-$575.

The Oompah Band

Trumpeter & Cymbals Bunnykins, DB87/88, 1990, £350-£450/$575-$745.

Drum Major/Sousaphone Bunnykins, DB86/90, 1990, £350-£450/$575-$745.

Drummer Bunnykins, DB108, 1991, £350-£450/$575-$745.

Drummer Bunnykins.. DB26 version 1, 1984-1990, £60-£80/ $100-$130. DB26 version 2, 1984, £140-£160/$230-$265. 50th Anniversary Inscription Produced in 1984 only.

Right: Drummer Bunnykins, DB89, 1990, £350-£450/$575-$745. UK Fairs Exclusive Limited Edition of 250 sets sold at the 8th Park Lane London Collectors Fair.

UKI Ceramics Exclusive Limited Edition of 250 sets. *Sousaphone* DB105 £120-£130/$000-$000; *Drum Major Bunnykins*, DB109, 1991, £350-£450/$575-$745. *Trumpeter* DB106 £350-£450/$575-$745; *Cymbals Bunnykins*, DB107, 1991, £350-£450/$575-$745.

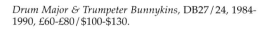

Drum Major & Trumpeter Bunnykins, DB27/24, 1984-1990, £60-£80/$100-$130.

Sousaphone & Cymbals Bunnykins, DB23/25, 1984-1990, £60-£80/100-$130.

Doctor Bunnykins DB181,
£30 / $50.

Dollie Bunnykins Playtime. DB8, 1972-1993, £60-£80 / $100-$130. DB80, 1988, £90-£100 / $150-$165. New colourway produced for Higbees, D H Holmes, Hornes, Strawbridge & Clothier USA. Special Backstamp for each.

Downhill Bunnykins, DB31, 1985-1988, £150-£180 / $250-$300.

Double Bass Player Bunnykins DB185

Family Photograph: Far Left: DB1, 1972-1988, £80-£100 / $130-$165. Left: DB67, 1988, £150-£180 / $250-$300.. Royal Doulton USA Special Colourway for Collectors Events.

Farmer Bunnykins, D6003, c1939-1940, £1500-£1800 / $2475-$2970.

Father Bunnykins, DB154, 1996, £30 / $50. Bunnykins of the Year 1996.

Father, Mother & Victoria Bunnykins, DB68, 1988-1996, £25-£30 / $40-$50.

Footballer Bunnykins, DB121, 1991, £350-£450 / $575-$745. UKI Ceramics Exclusive Limited Edition of 250, Paired with DB120.

Goalkeeper & Footballer Bunnykins, DB116 / DB117, 1991, £350-£450 / $575-$745. UKI Ceramics Exclusive of 250 sets (Australian Colourway).

Fireman Bunnykins, DB75, 1989-current, £20/$35.

Fisherman Bunnykins, DB84,1990-1993, £80-£100/ $130-$165

Freddie Bunnykins, D6024,1939-c1940, £2500-£3000/ $4125-$4950.

Freefall Bunnykins, DB41, 1986-1989, £220-£250/$365-$415.

Gardener Bunnykins, DB156, 1996-current, £20/$35.

Girl Skater Bunnykins, DB153, 1996-current, £25-£30 $40-$50.

Goalkeeper & Footballer Bunnykins, DB118/119, 1991, £350-£450/$575-$745 each. UKI Ceramics Exclusive Limited Edition of 250 pairs for sale in UK only.

Goalkeeper Bunnykins: DB120, 1991, £350-£450/$575-$745. DB122, 1991, £350-£450/ $575-$745. UKI Ceramics Exclusive Limited Editions of 250.

Goodnight Bunnykins, DB157, 1996-current, £20/$35.

Grandpa's Story, DB14, 1974-1983, £350-£450/$575-$745.

Groom Bunnykins, DB102, 1991-current, £20/$35.

Guardsman Bunnykins, DB127, 1992, £200-£220/$330-$365. UKI Ceramics Exclusive Limited Edition of 1000.

Halloween Bunnykins, DB132, 1993/current, £20-£25 $35-$45

Happy Birthday Bunnykins, DB21, 1984-1997, £20-£25/$35-$40.

Happy Birthday Bunnykins Music Box, DB36, 1985-1991, £120-£150/$200-$250. Plays "Happy Birthday to you".

Harry Bunnykins, DB73, 1988-1993, £40-£60/$65-$100

Home Run Bunnykins, DB43, 1983-1993, £60-£80/$100-$130.

Harry the Herald: DB95, 1990 £650-£750/$1080-$1240, UKI Ceramics Exclusive Limited Edition of 250 sold in a set (Bunnykins Royal Family DB91-95). Middle: DB115, 1991, £1000-£1200/$1650-$1980. Lambeth Productions Limited Edition of 300 sold at Collectors Event Toronto Canada. Right: DB49, 1986-1990, £80-£100/$130-$165.

Ice Cream Bunnykins, DB82, 1990-1993, £80-£100/$130-$165.

Irishman Bunnykins, DB178, 1998, £100-£120/$165-$200.

Jester Bunnykins, DB161, 1995, £300-£400/$495-$660. UKI Ceramics Exclusive Limited Edition of 1500.

Jockey Bunnykins, DB169, 1997, £100-£120. $165-$200 UKI Ceramics Exclusive Limited Edition of 2000.

Jogging Bunnykins, 1983-1989 £100-£120/$175-$210. Colour Variation (White Vest).

John Bull Bunnykins, DB134, 1993, £350-£450 $575-$745 . UKI Ceramics Exclusive Limited Edition of 1500.

Joker Bunnykins, DB171, 1997, £120-£150-$200-$250. UKI Ceramics Exclusive Limited Edition of 2500.

Juggler Bunnykins, DB164, 1996, £150-£180 / $250-$300. UKI Ceramics Exclusive Limited Edition of 1500.

King John Bunnykins. DB45, 1986-1990, £80-£100 / $130-$165. DB91, 1990, £650-£750 / $1080-$1240. UKI Ceramics Exclusive of 250 sets Bunnykins Royal Family DB91-95.

Knockout Bunnykins, DB30, 1985-1988, £200-£250 / $330-$415.

Lollipop Bunnykins, DB65, 1988-1991, £200-£250/$330-$415.

Mary Bunnykins, D6002, 1939-1940, £1500-£1800/$2475-$2970.

Magician Bunnykins, DB126, 1992, £200-£250/$330-$415. Commissioned by Pascoe & Co and Charles Dombeck USA Note Colourway of this figure commissioned by John Sinclair England DB159 and released in 1998.

Master Potter Bunnykins, DB131, 1993, £150-£200/ $250-$330. RDICC Exclusive.

Milkman Bunnykins, DB125, 1992, £650-£750/$1080-$1240. UKI Ceramics Exclusive of 1000.

Mother & Baby Bunnykins, DB167,
1997-current, £20/$35.

Mr Bunnykins at the Easter Parade,
DB51, 1986, £1000-£1200/$1650-
$1980. Special USA colourway.

Mothers Day Bunnykins, DB155,
1995-current, £20/$35.

Mr Bunnybeat Strumming, DB16,
1982-1988, £200-£220/ $330-$365.

Mr. Bunnykins at the Easter Parade,
DB18, 1982-1993, £40-£60/$65-$100.

Mr Bunnykins Autumn Days, DB5, 1972-1982, £350-£380 / $575-$625.

Mrs Bunnykins at the Easter Parade, DB52, 1986, £1500-£1800, $2475-$2970. Special USA colourway.

Mrs Bunnykins at the Easter Parade, DB19, 1982-1996, £25-£30 / $40-$50.

Mrs Bunnykins Clean Sweep, DB6, 1972-1991, £80-£100 / $130-$165.

New Baby Bunnykins, DB158, 1995-current, £20 / $35

Nurse Bunnykins, DB74, 1989-1994, £80-£100 $130-$165. Colour variation (no cross on apron). DB74 version 1 Red Cross, 1989-1994, £80-£100/$130-$165. DB74 version 2 Green Cross, 1994-current, £20/$35.

Out For a Duck Bunnykins, DB160, 1995, £160-£180/$265-$300. UKI Ceramics Exclusive Limited Edition of 1250.

Olympic Bunnykins. DB28, version 1, 1984-1988, £100-£120/$165-$200. DB28, version 2, 1984, £180-£200/ $300-$330. Australia only in 1984.

Paperboy Bunnykins, DB77, 1989-1993, £60-£80/$100-$130.

Partners in Collecting, DB151, 1995, £200-£300 / $3500-$525, Produced for RDICC USA 15th Anniversary.

Polly Bunnykins, DB71, 1988-1993, £40-£60 / $65-$100.

Policeman Bunnykins, DB64, 1988/ current, £20/$35 DISCONTINUED FEB 2000

Postman Bunnykins, DB76, 1989-1993, £80-£100/ $130-$165.

Prince Frederick Bunnykins. DB48, 1986-1990, £80-£100 / $130-$165. DB94, 1990, £650-£750/ $1080-$1240. UKI Ceramics Exclusive, Limited Edition of 250 sets. Bunnykins Royal Family DB91-95.

Princess Beatrice Bunnykins. DB47, 1986-1990, £80-£100/$130-$165. DB93, 1990, £650-£750/ $1080-$1240. UKI Ceramics Exclusive, Limited Edition of 250 sets. Bunnykins Royal Family DB91-95.

Queen Sophie Bunnykins. DB46, 1986-1990, £80-£100/$130-$165. DB92, 1990, £650-£750/ $1080-$1240. UKI Ceramics Exclusive, Limited Edition of 250 sets. Bunnykins Royal Family DB91-95.

Rainy Day Bunnykins, DB147, 1994-current, £20-£30/$35-$50.

Reggie Bunnykins, D6025, 19939-c1940s, £2500-£3000/ $4125-$4950.

Ring Master Bunnykins, DB165, 1996, £150-£180/$250-$300. UKI Ceramics Exclusive. Limited Edition of 1500.

Rise & shine, DB11, 1973-1988, £140-£160/$230-$265.

Sailor Bunnykins, DB166, 1997, £30/$50. Bunnykin of the Year 1997.

Rock & Roll Bunnykins, DB124, 1991, £600-£800 $990-$1320. Royal Doulton USA Exclusive. Limited Edition of 1000.

Santa Bunnykins Music Box,. DB34, 1985-1997, £120-£130/$200-£215. Plays "White Christmas".

Santa Bunnykins, DB17, 1981-1996, £25-£30/$40-$50.

Saxaphone Player Bunnykins, DB186, 1988.

Schooldays Bunnykins, DB57, 1987-1994, £40-£60 / $65-$100.

School Boy Bunnykins, DB66, 1988-1991, £120-£150 / $200-$250.

Schoolmaster Bunnykins, DB60, 1987-1996, £30-£40 / $50-$65.

Seaside Bunnykins, DB177, 1998, £20 / $35.

Scotsman Bunnykins, DB180, 1998, £100-£120 / $165-$200.

Sergeant Mountie Bunnykins, DB136, 1993, £1500-£1800 / $2475-$2970. Lambeth Productions Exclusive Limited Edition of 250 sold at Collectors Event Toronto Canada only.

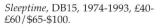

Sleeptime, DB15, 1974-1993, £40-£60 / $65-$100.

60th Anniversary Bunnykins, DB137, 1994 only, £60-£80/$105-$140.

Soccer Player Bunnykins, DB123, 1991, £350-£450/ $575-$745. UKI Exclusive limited edition of 250 paired with DB122.

Soldier Bunny bank. D6615 first version 1967-1977 £200-£250/ $330-$415. D6615 second version 1979-1981 £160-£180/$265-$300.

Storytime, DB59, 1987, £450-£550/$745-$910. Special colourway for Royal Doulton USA. Sold at collectors events only.

Susan Bunnykins DB70, 1988-1993, £60-£80/$100-$130.

Susan Bunnykins as Queen of the May, DB83, 1990-1992, £100-£120/$165-$200.

Sweetheart Bunnykins, DB130, 1992-1997, £30/$50.

Sweetheart Bunnykins, DB174, 1997 £120-£140/$165-$200.

Sydney Bunnykins, DB195, 1999-2000. Issue price £65.

Tally Ho! DB12, 1973-1988, £80-£100/$130-$165. DB12, 1973-1988, £80-£100/$140-$175. Colour variation (jacket should be maroon)

Tally Ho!, DB78, 1988, £120-£140/ $200-$230. Special colourway for Macey's USA.

Tally Ho! Music Box, DB53, 1983-1993, £90-£100/$000-$000. Plays "Rock a Bye Baby".

Below: *Touchdown Bunnykins:* Commissioned in 1990 by Gourmet Antiques USA in a special edition of 200 and sold as a set of five (DB96-DB100). Each £750-£950/$1240-$1565. *From left:* Ohio State University DB96; University of Michigan DB97; Cincinnati Bengals DB98; Notre Dame College DB99, University of Indiana DB100.

Touchdown Bunnykins Top: DB29 version 1, 1985-1988, £100 £120/$165-$200. Bottom: DB29 version 2, 1985, £1800-£2000/ $2970-$3300, 50 Special colourway produced for Regina Crafts USA in 1985 only.

Trick or Treat Bunnykins, DB162, 1995, £450-£550/ $745-$910 UKI Ceramics exclusive limited edition of 1500

The Artist, DB13, 1974-1982, £350-£450/$575-$745.

Tom Bunnykins, DB72, 1988-1993, £40-£60/ $65-$100.

Uncle Sam Teapot (Presidential Bunnykins), D6996, 1995, £60 £65/$100-$110. Exclusive to John Sinclair Limited Edition of 2500.

Uncle Sam Bunnykins, DB50, 1986-current, £35-£45/$60-$75. Available in the USA only.

Welsh Lady Bunnykins, DB172, 1997, £120-£150/$200-$250. Exclusive to UKI Ceramics, Limited Edition of 2500.

Wicket Keeper Bunnykins, DB150, 1994, £160-£180/ $265-$300. UKI exclusive limited edition of 1000.

William Bunnykins, DB69, 1988-1993, £40-£60/$65-$100.

Wizard Bunnykins, DB168, 1996, £250-£350/ $415-$575. UKI exclusive limited edition of 2000.

Selection of Bunnykins Publications with Bunnykins Collection name Plaques (Plaques where Exclusives issued by UKIC.

DMC Embroidery from Tableware Patterns

Bath Time

Baking

Bedtime Story

Daisy Chains

Picking Apples

Playing on the River

Playing with Doll's House

Raft

Ring-a-Ring o' Roses

DMC Embroidery from Tableware Patterns *continued*

Engine Pulling a Carriage.

Bunnykins Promotional gifts: Painting Book, Video & Record.

Punch & Judy

Original Artworks by Harry Sales (Colour Photocopy) sent to M&J after meeting Harry at Stafford Fair

Family in the Garden

Bunnykins Egg Shaped Box Large Size, 1979-1981

Needle Work by Jennifer Hutchison

Bunnykins Listings and Values

DB No	Version	Production Dates	Height	Market value	

Ace Bunnykins™ Designer Harry Sales *picture page 17*

| DB42 | 1 | 1986-1989 | 3¾" | £120-£130 | $200-$215 |

Aerobic Bunnykins™ Designer Harry Sales *picture page 17*

| DB40 | 1 | 1985-1988 | 2¾" | £90-£100 | $150-$165 |

Astro Bunnykins Rocket Man™ Designer Harry Sales *picture page 17*

| DB20 | 1 | 1983-1988 | 4¼" | £100-£120 | $165-$200 |
| DB35 | 1 | 1984-1989 | 7" | £80-£100 | $130-$165 |

Aussie Explorer Bunnykins™ Teapot Designer *picture page 17*
Exclusive to John Sinclair, Limited edition 2500

| D7027 | 1 | 1996 | 0" | £60 | $100 |

Aussie Surfer Bunnykins™ Designer Graham Tongue *picture page 17*

| DB133 | 1 | 1994 | 4" | £90-£100 | $150-$165 |

Australian Bunnykins™ Designer Harry Sales *picture page 17*

| DB58 | 1 | 1988 | 4" | £650-£750 | $1080-$1240 |

Ballerina Bunnykins™ Designer Graham Tongue *picture page 18*

| DB176 | 1 | 1998-Cur | 3½" | £20 | |

Ballet Bunnykins™ Designer Harry Sales

| DB44 | 1 | Not put into production | N/A | N/A | |

Banjo Player Bunnykins™ Designer Kim Curtis *picture page 18*
UKI Ceramics Exclusive limited edition of 2500. Part of the Jazz Band Collection

| DB182 | 1 | 1988-Cur | 5" | £58 | |

Bathtime Bunnykins™ Designer Graham Tongue *picture page 18*

| DB148 | 1 | 1994-1997 | 4" | £20-£30 | $35-$50 |

Batsman Bunnykins™ Designer Denise Andrews *picture page 18*
UKI Ceramics Exclusive Limited edition of 1000

| DB144 | 1 | 1994 | 4" | £160-£180 | $265-$300 |

Be Prepared Bunnykins™ Designer Graham Tongue *picture page 18*

| DB56 | 1 | 1987-1996 | 4" | £20-£30 | $35-$50 |

DB No	Version	Production Dates	Height	Market value		

Bedtime Bunnykins™ Designer Graham Tongue

picture page 19

DB No	Version	Production Dates	Height	Market value	
DB55	1	1987-cur	3¼"	£20	
DB63	2	1987	3¼"	£180-£200	$300-$330
DB79	3	1988	3¼"	£650-£750	$1080-$1240
DB103	4	1991	3¼"	£110-£120	$180-$200

Beefeater Bunnykins™ Designer
UKI Ceramics Exclusive limited edition of 1500

picture page 20

DB No	Version	Production Dates	Height	Market value	
DB163	1	1996		£180-£200	$300-$330

Billie & Buntie Bunnykins Sleigh Ride™
Designer Walter Hayward

picture page 19

DB No	Version	Production Dates	Height	Market value	
DB4	1	1972-1997	3¼"	£20	$35
DB81	2	1989	3½"	£160-£180	$265-$300

Billie Bunnykins Cooling Off™ Designer Walter Hayward

picture page 20

DB No	Version	Production Dates	Height	Market value	
DB3	1	1972-1987	3¾"	£200-£220	$330-$365

Billy Bunnykins™ Designer Charles Noke

picture page 20

DB No	Version	Production Dates	Height	Market value	
D6001	1	1939-c1940	4½"	£800-£1200	$1320-$1980

Bogey Bunnykins™ Designer Harry Sales

picture page 20

DB No	Version	Production Dates	Height	Market value	
DB32	1	1985-1992	4"	£100-£120	$165-$200

Bowler Bunnykins™ Designer Denise Andrews
UKI Ceramics Exclusive Limited edition of 1000

picture page 20

DB No	Version	Production Dates	Height	Market value	
DB145	1	1994	4"	£160-£180	$265-$300

Boy Skater Bunnykins™ Designer Martyn Alcock

picture page 21

DB No	Version	Production Dates	Height	Market value	
DB152	1	1995-1998	3½"	£20	$35

Bride Bunnykins™ Designer Graham Tongue

picture page 21

DB No	Version	Production Dates	Height	Market value
DB101	1	1991-cur	4"	£20

Bridesmaid Bunnykins™ Designer Graham Tongue

picture page 21

DB No	Version	Production Dates	Height	Market value
DB173	1	1997-cur	4"	£20

Brownie Bunnykins™ Designer Graham Tongue

picture page 21

DB No	Version	Production Dates	Height	Market value	
DB61	1	1987-1993	4"	£60-£80	$100-$130

Buntie Bunnykins Helping Mother™ Designer Walter Hayward

picture page 21

DB No	Version	Production Dates	Height	Market value	
DB2	1	1972-1993	3½"	£60-£80	$100-$130

DB No	Version	Production Dates	Height	Market value	

Busy Needles Bunnykins™ Designer Walter Hayward
picture page 22

| DB10 | 1 | 1973-1988 | 3¼" | £100-£120 | $165-$200 |

Carol Singer Bunnykins™ Designer Harry Sales
picture page 22
UKI Ceramics Exclusive Limited edition of 1000

| DB104 | 1 | 1991 | 4" | £200-£250 | $330-$415 |

Carol Singer Bunnykins™ Music Box Designer Harry Sales
picture page 22

| DB53 | 1 | 1986-1989 | 7" | £150-£200 | $250-$330 |

Cavalier Bunnykins™ Designer Graham Tongue
picture page 22
USA Limited edition of 2500

| DB179 | 1 | 1998 | 4½" | £180-£200 | $300-$330 |

Cheerleader Bunnykins™ Designer Denise Andrews
picture page 22
UKI Ceramics Exclusive Limited edition of 1000

| DB142 | 1 | 1994 | 4½" | £80-£100 | $130-$165 |
| DB143 | 1 | 1994 | 4½" | £80-£100 | $130-$165 |

Christmas Surprise Bunnykins™ Designer Graham Tongue

| DB146 | 1 | 1994-Cur | 3½" | £20 | |

City Gent Bunnykins™ Teapot Designer Unknown
picture page 22
Exclusive to John Sinclair, Limited edition of 2500

| D6966 | 1 | 1994 | 8" | £75-£80 | $125-$130 |

Clarinet Player Bunnykins™ Designer Kim Curtis
picture page 23
UKI Ceramics Exclusive limited edition of 2500. Part of the Jazz Band Collection

| DB184 | 1 | 1988-Cur | 5" | £58 | |

Clown Bunnykins™ Designer Denise Andrews
picture page 23
UKI Ceramics Exclusive Limited edition of 250 and 750

| DB128 | 1 | 1992 | 4¼" | £650-£750 | $1080-$1240 |
| DB129 | 2 | 1992 | 4¼" | £1200-£1500 | $1980-$2475 |

Collector Bunnykins™ Designer Harry Sales
picture page 23

| DB54 | 1 | 1987 | 4¼" | £600-£650 | $990-$1080 |

Constable Mountie Bunnykins™ Designer Graham Tongue
Limited edition of 750
picture page 23

| DB135 | 1 | 1993 | 4" | £650-£750 | $1080-$1240 |

Cook Bunnykins™ Designer Graham Tongue

| DB85 | 1 | 1990-1994 | 4¼" | £40-£60 | $65-$100 |

DB No	Version	Production Dates	Height	Market value	

Cymbals Bunnykins™ Designer Harry Sales   *picture page 24*

DB No	Version	Production Dates	Height	Market value	
DB25	1	1984-1990	3½"	£60-£80	$100-$130
DB88	1	1990	3½"	£350-£450	$575-$745
DB107	1	1991	4"	£350-£450	$575-$745

Daisie Bunnykins Springtime™ Designer Walter Hayward   *picture page 23*

DB No	Version	Production Dates	Height	Market value	
DB7	1	1972-1983	3½"	£300-£350	$495-$575

Doctor Bunnykins™ Designer Martyn Alcock   *picture page 26*

DB No	Version	Production Dates	Height	Market value
DB181	1	1988-Cur	5"	£30

Dollie Bunnykins Playtime™ Designer Walter Hayward   *picture page 26*

DB No	Version	Production Dates	Height	Market value	
DB8	1	1972-1993	4"	£60-£80	$100-$130
DB80	2	1988	4"	£90-£100	$150-$165

Double Bass Player Bunnykins™ Designer Kim Curtis   *picture page 26*
UKI Ceramics Exclusive limited edition of 2500. Part of the Jazz Band Collection

DB No	Version	Production Dates	Height	Market value
DB185	1	1988-Cur	5"	£n/a

Downhill Bunnykins™ Designer Harry Sales   *picture page 26*

DB No	Version	Production Dates	Height	Market value	
DB31	1	1985-1988	2½"	£150-£180	$250-$300

Drum-Major Bunnykins™ Designer Harry Sales   *picture pages 24/25*

DB No	Version	Production Dates	Height	Market value	
DB27	1	1984-1990	3½"	£60-£80	$100-$130
DB90	2	1990	3¾"	£350-£450	$575-$745
DB109	3	1991	3½"	£350-£450	$575-$745

Drummer Bunnykins™ Designer Harry Sales   *picture page 24*

DB No	Version	Production Dates	Height	Market value	
DB26	1	1984-1990	3½"	£60-£80	$100-$130
DB26[1]	2	1984	3¾"	£140-£160	$230-$265
DB89	3	1990	3¾"	£350-£450	$575-$745
DB108	4	1991	3½"''	£350-£450	$575-$745

[1]Jubilee edition

Easter Greetings Bunnykins™ Designer Graham Tongue   *picture page 26*

DB No	Version	Production Dates	Height	Market value
DB149	1	1995-cur	3½"	£20

Family Photograph Bunnykins™ Designer Walter Hayward   *picture page 26*

DB No	Version	Production Dates	Height	Market value	
DB1	1	1972-1988	4½"	£80-£100	$130-$165
DB67	2	1988	4½"	£150-£180	$250-$300

Farmer Bunnykins™ Designer Charles Noke   *picture page 27*

DB No	Version	Production Dates	Height	Market value	
D6003	1	1939-c1940s	7½"	£1500-£1800	$2475-$2970

DB No	Version	Production Dates	Height	Market value		

Father Bunnykins™ Designer Martyn Alcock
Bunnykins of the Year 1996

picture page 28

D154	1	1996	4"	£30	$50

Father, Mother and Victoria Bunnykins™
Designer Walter Hayward

picture page 29

DB68	1	1988-1996	4½"	£25-£30	$40-$50

Footballer Bunnykins™ Designer Denise Andrews
UKI Ceramics Exclsuive Limited edition of 250

picture page 27/30

117	1	1991	4½"	£350-£450	$575-$745
119	2	1991	4½"	£350-£450	$575-$745
121	3	1991	4½"	£350-£450	$575-$745

Fireman Bunnykins™ Designer Graham Tongue

picture page 28

DB75	1	1989-Cur	4¼"	£20

Fisherman Bunnykins™ Designer Graham Tongue

picture page 28

DB84	1	1990-1993	4¼"	£80-£100	$130-$165
DB170	2	1997-Cur	4"	£20	

Freddie Bunnykins™ Designer Charles Noke

picture page 28

D6024	1	1939-c1940s	3¾"	£2500-£3000	$4125-$4950

Freefall Bunnykins™ Designer Harry Sales

picture page 29

DB41	1	1986-1989	3¾"	£220-£250	$365-$415

Gardener Bunnykins™ Designer Warren Platt

picture page 30

DB156	1	1996-1998		£20	$35

Girl Skater Bunnykins™ Designer Martyn Alcock

picture page 29

DB153	1	1995-1997	3½"	£25-£30	$40-$50

Goalkeeper Bunnykins™ Designer Denise Andrews
UKI Ceramics Exclsuive Limited edition of 250

picture page 27/30

DB116	1	1991	4½"	£350-£450	$575-$745
DB118	2	1991	4½"	£350-£450	$575-$745
DB120	3	1991	4½"	£350-£450	$575-$745
DB122	4	1991	4½"	£350-£450	$575-$745

Goodnight Bunnykins™ Designer Graham Tongue

picture page 29

DB157	1	1995-cur	3½"	£20

DB No	Version	Production Dates	Height	Market value		

Grandpa's Story Bunnykins™ Designer Walter Hayward — *picture page 30*

DB14	1	1974-1983	4″	£350-£450	$575-$745

Groom Bunnykins™ Designer Graham Tongue — *picture page 30*

DB102	1	1991-cur	4½″	£20	

Guardsman Bunnykins™ Designer Denise Andrews — *picture page 30*
UKI Ceramics Exclsuive Limited edition of 1000

DB127	1	1992	4½″	£200-£220	$330-$365

Halloween Bunnykins™ Designer Graham Tongue — *picture page 30*

DB132	1	1993-1997	3¼″	£20-£25	$35-$40

Happy Birthday Bunnykins™ Designer Harry Sales — *picture page 30*

DB21	1	1983-1997	3¾″	£20-£25	$35-$40

Happy Birthday Bunnykins™ Music Box Designer Harry Sales — *picture page 31*

DB36	1	1984-1993	7″	£120-£150	$200-$250

Harry Bunnykins™ Designer Graham Tongue — *picture page 31*

DB73	1	1988-1993	3″	£40-£60	$65-$100

Harry The Herald™ Designer Harry Sales — *picture page 31*

DB49	1	1986-1990	3½″	£80-£100	$130-$165
DB95	2	1990	3½″	£650-£750	$1080-$1240
DB115	3	1991	3½″	£1000-£1200	$1650-$1980

Home Run Bunnykins™ Designer Harry Sales — *picture page 31*

DB43	1	1986-1993	4″	£60-£80	$100-$130

Ice Cream Bunnykins™ Designer Graham Tongue — *picture page 32*

DB82	1	1990-1993	4½″	£80-£100	$130-$165

Irishman Bunnykins™ Designer Denise Andrews — *picture page 32*
UKI Ceramics Exclusive Limited edition of 2500

DB178	1	1998	5″	£100-£120	$165-$200

Japanese Lady Bunnykins™ Teapot Designer Unknown
Exclusive to John Sinclair, Limited edition of 2500

Unk[1]	1	1998	8″	£69	

[1]Details unknown as announced as going to Press

DB No	Version	Production Dates	Height	Market value		

Jester Bunnykins™ Designer Denise Andrews   *picture page 32*
UKI Ceramics ExclusiveLimited edition of 1500

DB No	Version	Production Dates	Height	Market value		
DB161	1	1995	4½"	£300-£400	$495-$660	

Jockey Bunnykins™ Designer Denise Andrews   *picture page 32*
UKI Ceramics Exclusive limited edtion of 2000

| DB169 | 1 | 1997 | | £100-£120 | $165-$200 | |

Jogging Bunnykins™ Designer Harry Sales   *picture page 32*

| DB22 | 1 | 1983-1989 | 2½" | £100-£120 | $165-$200 | |

Jogging Bunnykins™ **Music Box** Designer Harry Sales

| DB37 | 1 | 1987-1989 | 5½" | £120-£150 | $200-$250 | |

John Bull Bunnykins™ Designer Denise Andrews   *picture page 33*
UKI Ceramics Exclusive Limited edition of 1000

| DB134 | 1 | 1993 | 4½" | £350-£450 | $575-$745 | |

Joker Bunnykins™ Designer Denise Andrews   *picture page 33*
UKI Ceramics ExclusiveLimited edition of 2500

| DB171 | 1 | 1997 | 5" | £120-£150 | $200-$250 | |

Juggler Bunnykins™ Designer Denise Andrews   *picture page 33*
UKI Ceramics Exclusive limited edition of 1500

| DB164 | 1 | 1996 | | £150-£180 | $250-$300 | |

King John™ Designer Harry Sales   *picture page 33*

| DB45 | 1 | 1986-1990 | 4" | £80-£100 | $130-$165 | |
| DB91 | 2 | 1990 | 4" | £650-£750 | $1080-$1240 | |

Knockout Bunnykins™ Designer Harry Sales   *picture page 33*

| DB30 | 1 | 1985-1988 | 4" | £200-£250 | $330-$415 | |

Lollipop Bunnykins™ Designer Graham Tongue   *picture page 34*

| DB65 | 1 | 1988-1991 | 3¾" | £200-£250 | $330-$415 | |

Magician Bunnykins™ Designer Graham Tongue   *picture page 34*
DB126 – Commissioned by Pascoe & Co, limited edition of 1000.
DB159 – Colourway commissioned by John Sinclair, England, not issued.

| DB126 | 1 | 1992 | 4½" | £200-£250 | $330-$415 | |
| DB159 | 2 | 1998 | 4½" | | | |

Mary Bunnykins™ Designer Charles Noke   *picture page 34*

| D6002 | 1 | 1939-c1940 | 6½" | £1500-£1800 | $2475-$2970 | |

DB No	Version	Production Dates	Height	Market value	

Master Potter Bunnykins™ Designer Graham Tongue   *picture page 34*

| DB131 | 1 | 1993 | 3¾″ | £150-£200 | $250-$330 |

Milkman Bunnykins™ Designer Graham Tongue   *picture page 34*
UKI Ceramics Exclsutive Limited edition of 1000

| DB125 | 1 | 1992 | 4½″ | £650-£750 | $1080-$1240 |

Mother and Baby Bunnykins™ Designer Shane Ridge   *picture page 35*

| DB167 | 1 | 1997-Cur | | £20 | |

Mother Bunnykins™ Designer Charles Noke

| D6004 | 1 | 1939-c1940s | 7″ | £1500-£1800 | $2475-$2970 |

Mother's Day Bunnykins™ Designer Shane Ridge   *picture page 35*

| DB155 | 1 | 1995-cur | 4″ | £20 | |

Mr Bunnybeat Strumming™ Designer Harry Sales   *picture page 35*

| DB16 | 1 | 1982-1988 | 4½″ | £200-£220 | $330-$365 |

Mr Bunnybeat Strumming™ Music Box Designer Harry Sales

| DB38 | 1 | 1987-1989 | 7½″ | £180-£200 | $300-$330 |

Mr Bunnykins at the Easter Parade™ Designer Harry Sales   *picture page 35*

| DB18 | 1 | 1982-1993 | 5″ | £40-£60 | $65-$100 |
| DB51 | 2 | 1986 | 5″ | £1000-£1200 | $1650-$1980 |

Mr Bunnykins Autumn Days™ Designer Walter Hayward   *picture page 36*

| DB5 | 1 | 1972-1982 | 4″ | £350-£380 | $575-$625 |

Mrs Bunnykins at the Easter Parade™ Designer Harry Sales   *picture page 36*

| DB19 | 1 | 1982-1996 | 4½″ | £25-£30 | $40-$50 |
| DB52 | 2 | 1986 | 4½″ | £1500-£1800 | $2475-$2970 |

Mrs Bunnykins at the Easter Parade™ Music Box Designer Harry Sales

| DB39 | 1 | 1987-1991 | 7″ | £100-£120 | $165-$200 |

Mrs Bunnykins Clean Sweep™ Designer Walter Hayward   *picture page 36*

| DB6 | 1 | 1972-1991 | 4″ | £80-£100 | $130-$165 |

New Baby Bunnykins™ Designer Grahame Tongue   *picture page 36*

| DB158 | 1 | 1995-cur | 4″ | £20 | |

DB No	Version	Production Dates	Height	Market value	

Nurse Bunnykins™ Designer Graham Tongue   *picture page 37*

DB No	Version	Production Dates	Height	Market value	
DB74[1]	1	1989-1994	4¼″	£80-£100	$130-$165
DB74[2]	2	1989-cur	4¼″	£20	

[1] Red Cross – [2] Green Cross

Olympic Bunnykins™ Designer Harry Sales   *picture page 37*

DB No	Version	Production Dates	Height	Market value	
DB28[1]	1	1984-1988	3¾″	£100-£120	$165-$200
DB28[2]	2	1984	3½″	£180-£200	$300-$330

[1] White and blue – [2] Gold and green

Out for a Duck™ Designer Denise Andrews   *picture page 37*
UKI Ceramics Exclsutive Limited edition of 1250

DB No	Version	Production Dates	Height	Market value	
DB160	1	1995	4½″	£160-£180	$265-$300

Paperboy Bunnykins™ Designer Graham Tongue   *picture page 37*

DB No	Version	Production Dates	Height	Market value	
DB77	1	1989-1993	4″	£60-£80	$100-$130

Partners in Collecting™   *See under Storytime Bunnykins*   *picture page 38*

Policeman Bunnykins™ Designer Graham Tongue   *picture page 38*

DB No	Version	Production Dates	Height	Market value	
DB64	1	1988-Cur	4¼″	£20	

Polly Bunnykins™ Designer Graham Tongue   *picture page 38*

DB No	Version	Production Dates	Height	Market value	
DB71	1	1988-1993	3½″	£40-£60	$65-$100

Postman Bunnykins™ Designer Graham Tongue   *picture page 38*

DB No	Version	Production Dates	Height	Market value	
DB76	1	1989-1993	4½″	£80-£100	$130-$165

President Bunnykins™ Teapot *See under Uncle Sam Bunnykins*

Prince Frederick™ Designer Harry Sales   *picture page 38*

DB No	Version	Production Dates	Height	Market value	
DB48	1	1986-1990	3½″	£80-£100	$130-$165
DB94	2	1990	3½″	£650-£750	$1080-$1240

Princess Beatrice™ Designer Harry Sales   *picture page 39*

DB No	Version	Production Dates	Height	Market value	
DB47	1	1986-1990	3½″	£80-£100	$130-$165
DB93	2	1990	3½″	£650-£750	$1080-$1240

Queen Sophie™ Designer Harry Sales   *picture page 39*

DB No	Version	Production Dates	Height	Market value	
DB46	1	1986-1990	4½″	£80-£100	$130-$165
DB92	2	1990	4½″	£650-£750	$1080-$1240

Rainy Day Bunnykins™ Designer Graham Tongue   *picture page 39*

DB No	Version	Production Dates	Height	Market value	
DB147	1	1994-1997	4″	£20-£30	$35-$50

DB No	Version	Production Dates	Height	Market value	

Reggie Bunnykins™ Designer Charles Noke
picture page 39

| D6025 | 1 | 1939-c1940s | 3¾" | £2500-£3000 | $4125-$4950 |

Ringmaster Bunnykins™ Designer Denise Andrews
picture page 39
UKI Ceramics Exclusive limited edition of 1500

| DB165 | 1 | 1996 | | £150-£180 | $250-$300 |

Rise and Shine Bunnykins™ Designer Walter Hayward
picture page 40

| DB11 | 1 | 1973-1988 | 3¾" | £140-£160 | $230-$265 |

Rock 'n' Roll Bunnykins™ Designer Harry Sales
picture page 40
Limited edition of 1000 for the USA Rock & Roll Hall of Fame
Renamed version of Mr Bunnybeat Strumming DB16

| DB124 | 1 | 1991 | 4½" | £600-£800 | $990-$1320 |

Sailor Bunnykins™ Designer Graham Tongue
picture page 40
Bunnykin of the Year 1997

| DB166 | 1 | 1997 | 2½" | £30 | $50 |

Santa Bunnykins Happy Christmas™ Designer Harry Sales
DB62 is a limited edition Christmas Tree ornament
picture page 40

| DB17 | 1 | 1981-1996 | 4½" | £25-£30 | $40-$50 |
| DB62 | 1 | 1987 | 4" | £1500-£1800 | $2475-$2970 |

Santa Bunnykins™ Music Box Designer Harry Sales
picture page 40

| DB34 | 1 | 1984-1991 | 7¼" | £120-£130 | $200-$215 |

Saxaphone Player Bunnykins™ Designer Kim Curtis
picture page 40
UKI Ceramics Exclusive limited edition of 2500. Part of the Jazz Band Collection

| DB186 | 1 | 1988-Cur | 5" | £n/a | $n/a |

School Boy Bunnykins™ Designer Graham Tongue
picture page 41

| DB66 | 1 | 1988-1991 | 4" | £120-£150 | $200-$250 |

Schooldays Bunnykins™ Designer Graham Tongue
picture page 41

| DB57 | 1 | 1987-1994 | 3½" | £40-£60 | $65-$100 |

Schoolmaster Bunnykins™ Designer Graham Tongue
picture page 41

| DB60 | 1 | 1987-1996 | 4" | £30-£40 | $50-$65 |

Scotsman Bunnykins™ Designer Denise Andrews
picture page 41
UKI Ceramics Exclusive Limited edition of 2500

| DB180 | 1 | 1998 | 4½" | £100-£120 | $165-$200 |

DB No	Version	Production Dates	Height	Market value	

Seaside Bunnykins™ Designer Martyn Alcock
picture page 41
Bunnykins of the Year 1998

| DB177 | 1 | 1998 | 3″ | £20 | $35 |

Sergeant Mountie Bunnykins™ Designer Graham Tongue
picture page 41
Limited edition of 250

| DB136 | 1 | 1993 | 4″ | £1500-£1800 | $2475-$2970 |

Sixtieth Anniversary of Bunnykins™ Designer Denise Andrews
picture page 42

| DB137 | 1 | 1994 | 4½″ | £60-£80 | $100-$130 |

Sleepytime™ Designer Walter Hayward
picture page 41

| DB15 | 1 | 1974-1993 | 1¾″ | £40-£60 | $65-$100 |

Soccer Player Bunnykins™ Designer Denise Andrews
picture page 42
UKI Ceramics limited edition of 250 (paired with DB122)

| DB123 | 4 | 1991 | 4½″ | £350-£450 | $575-$745 |

Soldier Bunny Bank™ Designer Unknown
picture page 42

| D6615 | 1 | 1967-1977 | 8½″ | £200-£250 | $330-$415 |
| D6615 | 1 | 1979-1981 | 9¼″ | £160-£180 | $265-$300 |

Sousaphone Bunnykins™ Designer Harry Sales
picture page 25

DB23	1	1984-1990	3½″	£60-£80	$100-$130
DB86	1	1990	3½″	£350-£450	$575-$745
DB105	1	1991	4″	£350-£450	$575-$745

Storytime Bunnykins™ Designer Walter Hayward
picture page 42
DB151 renamed **Partners in Collecting** colourway for US RDICC 15th anniversary

DB9	1	1972-1997	3″	£20-£30	$35-$50
DB59	2	1987	3″	£450-£550	$745-$910
DB151	3	1995	3″	£200-£300	$330-$495

Susan Bunnykins™ Designer Walter Hayward
picture page 42

| DB70 | 1 | 1988-1993 | 3¼″ | £60-£80 | $100-$130 |

Susan Bunnykins as Queen of the May™
Designer Graham Tongue
picture page 43

| DB83 | 1 | 1990-1991 | 4″ | £100-£120 | $165-$200 |

Sweetheart Bunnykins™ Designer Graham Tongue
picture page 43
DB174 – UK Fairs Ltd Exclusive Limited edition of 2500

| DB130 | 1 | 1992-1997 | 3¾″ | £30 | $50 |
| DB174 | 2 | 1997 | 4" | £100-£120 | $165-$200 |

DB No	Version	Production Dates	Height	Market value	

Sydney Bunnykins™ Designers Brian Dalglish, Bill Bryant and
Jeffrey Bartholomeusz   *picture page 43*
Commissioned by Dalbry Antiques & Collectibles, Melbourne, Australia. Limited edition of 2500 with exclusive backstamp.

DB No	Version	Production Dates	Height	Market value
DB195	1	1999-2000	4¾"	£65

Tally Ho! Bunnykins™ Designer Walter Hayward   *picture page 43*

DB No	Version	Production Dates	Height	Market value	
DB12	1	1973-1988	3¾"	£80-£100	$130-$165
DB78	2	1988	4"	£120-£140	$200-$230

Tally Ho! Bunnykins™ Music Box Designer Walter Hayward   *picture page 44*

DB No	Version	Production Dates	Height	Market value	
DB33[1]	1	1984-1993	7"	£120-£150	$200-$250
DB33[2]	2	1988-1991	7"	£120-£150	$200-$250

[1] Red coat, yellow jumper – [2] Red coat, brown trousers and maroon tie

The Artist Bunnykins™ Designer Walter Hayward   *picture page 45*

DB No	Version	Production Dates	Height	Market value	
DB13	1	1974-1982	3¾"	£350-£450	$575-$745

Tom Bunnykins™ Designer Graham Tongue   *picture page 45*

DB No	Version	Production Dates	Height	Market value	
DB72	1	1988-1993	3"	£40-£60	$65-$100

Touchdown Bunnykins™ Designer Harry Sales   *picture page 44*
DB96-100 inclusive were issued as a limited edition of 200 each

DB No	Version	Production Dates	Height	Market value	
DB29[1]	1	1985-1988	3¼"	£100-£120	$165-$200
DB29[2]	2	1985	3¼"	£1800-£2000	$2970-$3300
DB96	3	1990	3¼"	£750-£950	$1240-$1565
DB97	4	1990	3¼"	£750-£950	$1240-$1565
DB98	5	1990	3¼"	£750-£950	$1240-$1565
DB99	6	1990	3¼"	£750-£950	$1240-$1565
DB100	7	1990	3½"	£750-£950	$1240-$1565

[1] Blue and White – [2] Maroon and gold, limited edition of 50 for Boston College

Trick or Treat Bunnykins™ Designer Denise Andrews   *picture page 45*
UKI Ceramics Exclusive limited edtion of 1500

DB No	Version	Production Dates	Height	Market value	
DB162	1	1995		£450-£550	$745-$910

Trumpeter Bunnykins™ Designer Harry Sales   *picture page 24/25*

DB No	Version	Production Dates	Height	Market value	
DB24	1	1984-1990	3½"	£60-£80	$100-$130
DB87	1	1990	3¾"	£350-£450	$575-$745
DB106	1	1991	3¾"	£350-£450	$575-$745

DB No	Version	Production Dates	Height	Market value	

Uncle Sam Bunnykins™ Designer Harry Sales
picture page 45

USA only

DB No	Version	Production Dates	Height	Market value	
DB50	1	1986-cur	4½″	£35	$60
DB175[1]	2	1997	4½″	£180-£200	$300-$330
DB [2]		1998	4½″	£250-£300	$300-$400

[1] Exclusive USA colourway for Pascoe & Co and Seaway China
[2] Exclusive USA colourway for New England Chapter

Uncle Sam Bunnykins™ Teapot (also known as Presidential)
picture page 45

Exclsuive to John Sinclair, limited edition of 2500

DB No	Version	Production Dates	Height	Market value	
D6996	1	1995		£60-£65	$100-$110

Welsh Lady Bunnykins™ Designer Denise Andrews
picture page 46

UKI Ceramics Exclusive Limited edition of 2500

DB No	Version	Production Dates	Height	Market value	
DB172	1	1997	5″	£120-£150	$200-$250

Wicket Keeper Bunnykins™ Designer Denise Andrews
picture page 46

UKI Ceramics Exclusive Limited edition of 1000

DB No	Version	Production Dates	Height	Market value	
DB150	1	1994	3½″	£160-£180	$265-$300

William Bunnykins™ Designer Walter Hayward
picture page 46

DB No	Version	Production Dates	Height	Market value	
DB69	1	1988-1993	3¾″	£40-£60	$65-$100

Wizard Bunnykins™ Designer Denise Andrews
picture page 46

UKI Ceramics Exclusive Limited Edition of 2000

DB No	Version	Production Dates	Height	Market value	
DB168	1	1996		£250-£350	$415-$575

Bunnykins Resin Figures

Royal Doulton introduced a series of Bunnykins figures made from resin in 1996 and 1997

DB No	Height	Market value	

Harry Bunnykins A Little Bunny at Play™

DBR1	1¾"	£15-£20	$25-$35

Harry Bunnykins Playtime™

DBR2	2"	£15-£20	$25-$35

Reginald Ratley Up To No Good™

DBR3	2¼"	£15-£20	$25-$35

Susan Bunnykins The Helper™

DBR4	3"	£15-£20	$25-$35

William Bunnykins Asleep in the Sun™

DBR5	2¼"	£15-£20	$25-$35

Lady Ratley Her Ladyship Explains™

DBR6	3¼"	£20-£25	$35-$40

Mrs Bunnykins A Busy Morning Shopping™

DBR7	2½"	£20-£25	$35-$40

Father Bunnykins Home From Work™

DBR8	3¾"	£20-£25	$35-$40

William Bunnykins A Bunny in a Hurry™

DBR9	2¼"	£15-£20	$25-$35

Susan Bunnykins Wildlife Spotting™

DBR10	2¾"	£15-£20	$25-$35

Susan and Harry Bunnykins Minding the Baby Brother™

DBR11	2½"	£20-£25	$35-$40

Father Bunnykins and Harry Decorating the Tree™

DBR12	4"	£30-£40	$50-$65

Mrs Bunnykins and William The Birthday Cake™

DBR13	3¼"	£20-£25	$35-$40

Happy Christmas from the Bunnykins Family™

| DBR14 | 6" | £100-£120 | $165-$200 |

Picnic Time with the Bunnykins Family™

| DBR15 | 5" | £100-£120 | $165-$200 |

Birthday Girl™

| DBR16 | 1½" | £15-£20 | $25-$35 |

Birthday Boy™

| DBR17 | 1½" | £15-£20 | $25-$35 |

The New Baby™

| DBR18 | 3½" | £20-£25 | $35-$40 |

The Rocking Horse™

| DBR19 | 2¾" | £15-£20 | $25-$35 |

Photograph Frame – Girl™

| DBR20 | 5¼" | £15-£20 | $25-$35 |

Photograph Frame – Boy™

| DBR21 | 5¼" | £15-£20 | $25-$35 |

The Story of Beatrix Potter Figures

Beatrix Potter was born in London in 1866 to well-to-do middle class parents. She was considered to be a delicate child and educated at home by a series of governesses. Her rather solitary existence was enlivened by a talent for drawing which showed itself at an early age. Luckily for future generations this talent was encouraged by her parents. Her early models were the assortment of pets, which she and her younger brother accumulated. Family holidays in the Lake District and Scotland stimulated her interest in the natural world which she recorded in paintings and drawings. When away from London Beatrix would write letters to the children she knew, many of whom were the children of her former governesses. One such letter sent on 4th September 1893 was to prove rather important. The recipient was five year old Noel Moore. The letter was an attempt to cheer up Noel who was ill and told the story of a rabbit called Peter. Evidently the letter pleased Master Moore because he still had it eight years later. Beatrix borrowed back the letter intending to turn it into a book. She was unable to find a publisher but undaunted she had 250 copies printed privately which she sent to family and friends for Christmas 1901. In the meantime she continued to search for a commercial publisher. The search ended in 1902 when an agreement was reached with Frederick Warne and Co. The book was re-illustrated in colour and published in October1902 in an edition of 8000 copies. Within a matter of months 28,000 copies had been printed. *The Tale of Peter Rabbit* was followed in 1903 by *The Tale of Squirrel Nutkin*. For the next few years an average of two new books a year were published. Also at this time the first Beatrix Potter character merchandise appeared which included a board game, wall paper designs and a Peter Rabbit soft toy.

Beatrix Potter's editor at Frederick Warne was Norman Warne. They developed a close relationship and in 1905 Norman proposed. Beatrix's parents did not approve but nevertheless she accepted. However the marriage was not to be. Norman died suddenly only a few weeks later. Naturally heartbroken Beatrix turned to her work for comfort, producing three more books. She also bought a property in the Lake District where she spent more and more of her spare time, the countryside providing the background for many of her books. Family committments eventually brought her back to London but she continued to produce her books – eleven more in seven years.

The royalties from her books allowed Beatrix to buy more properties in the Lake District. In the course of doing this she met a local solicitor, William Heelis. On 15th October 1913 they were married. The Lake District became her home and farming her life. Only five more books were written. Beatrix Potter died on 22nd December 1943. By now her Lake District estate amounted to 4000 acres which she left to The National Trust.

The First Attempts to Produce Beatrix Potter Figures

It can be seen from the earliest days of her success that Beatrix Potter felt that there was scope for her creations to be lifted off the printed page and into other marketable products. There was an attempt around 1907 to produce ceramic models of her characters. She had modelled some clay figures and had contacted Royal Doulton's Lambeth pottery with a view to having them reproduced. Nothing came of this project as there was already an agreement with a German firm to make a range of nurseryware based on her characters. Miss Potter did not like the German product and attempts were made to cancel or alter the agreement. About ten years later there was another abortive attempt to make Beatrix Potter character figures.

A Stoke on Trent firm, Grimwades, sent Beatrix a model of Jemima Puddle Duck. She did not approve of it but was interested enough to pursue the matter a little more. She sent to the factory some clay figures she had modelled herself. It is not clear if these were the same figures she had taken to Royal Doulton. The figures were damaged in transit but enough survived to allow Grimwades to see what she had in mind. Another model of Jemima Puddle Duck was made which Beatrix liked better. However this time she did not like the colouring. It was then suggested that there could be some sort of co-operation between Grimwades and Royal Doulton who had more experience in colouring figures. It is recorded that Beatrix liked this idea but nothing came of it. It would seem that Royal Doulton was destined to become involved in producing Beatrix Potter figures but the final connection was still some years away and only happened after Beatrix Potter had died and even then as a result of a factory takeover.

Beswick Beatrix Potter Figures

It was another Stoke on Trent pottery which finally succeeded in producing the first acceptable range of Beatrix Potter figures. The Beswick factory was founded in 1894. Initially it manufactured domestic wares in both china and earthenware but became most well known for its animal models and novelties. The idea to create a range of Beatrix Potter figures came from Lucy Beswick, wife of the chairman and Managing Director of the company. Mrs Beswick was born in Cumbria and the family often returned to the Lake District for holidays. It was on one of these visits that Mrs. Beswick visited the home of Beatrix Potter. On returning to the potteries she suggested to the company's chief modeller, Arthur Gredington, that Jemima Puddle-Duck would make an attractive figure. A suggestion from the chairman's wife was obviously not one to be ignored and a clay model was duly produced. Having secured the approval of Mr. Beswick and the other directors, and copyright permission obtained from Frederick Warne and Co., further characters were modelled. The first collection consisted of ten of the most popular characters. Jemima Puddle-Duck, Peter Rabbit, Tom Kitten, Timmy Tiptoes, Squirrel Nutkin, Mrs. Tittlemouse, Little Pig Robinson, Benjamin Bunny, Samuel Whiskers and Mrs. Tiggywinkle. Great care was taken to be true to the original illustrations both in terms of modelling and colouring.

The figures were ready in 1948 but because war-time restrictions on the sale of decorative china in the home market, the figures had to be launched abroad. The reaction from customers was tremendous, with much comment on how accurately they had been transferred from the printed page. More models were added to the collection but it was not until 1977 that all the Beatrix Potter tales had contributed characters. The first figure to be discontinued was in 1967. This was, of course, the 1955 introduction **Duchess** (P1355) which now commands a noteworthy price on the secondary market.

Royal Doulton Take Over

The Beswick company was sold to Royal Doulton in 1969 but the Beatrix Potter figures continued to be marketed under the Beswick backstamp until 1989 when they were transferred to Royal Albert. To those outside the Royal Doulton group this move was perceived as a little odd as Royal Albert had hitherto been best known for its range of rather flowery and ornate tableware. No doubt Royal Doulton had its reasons but to the best of my knowledge they have never made them public. The change to Royal Albert has proved to be relatively shortlived as the range is currently being returned to the Beswick backstamp. Nevertheless after the previous failed attempts Royal Doulton has, since 1969, been responsible for producing ceramic Beatrix Potter figures albeit under a different name. No doubt Miss Potter would finally approve.

Other Items are Added to the Collection

The success of the figures spawned other Beatrix Potter ceramic items. The first to appear was a lamp base in the shape of a tree. This was sold on its own or with a choice of figure. The wood theme was continued in 1970 when a display base for six Beatrix Potter figures was introduced. It is modelled in the form of gnarled and knotted wood.

On two occasions Beswick produced wall plaques featuring Beatrix Potter characters. The first time was in 1967 when three subjects were modelled, the plaque taking the form of the character. They only remained in production for two years but in 1977 another three subjects were tried, this time as relief moulded square plaques. Again they only met with limited success.

More success was achieved with the introduction in 1989 and 1990 of a set of six character jugs based on Beatrix Potter characters. Attractive and charming though they undoubtedly are, one cannot help wonder what Miss Potter might have thought of this concept, bearing in mind her concern over the original attempts to produce ceramic figures.

Another short-lived experiment was the collection of Studio Sculptures introduced in 1984 and 1985. These were seven Beatrix Potter characters modelled in great detail and cast in a 'bonded ceramic' body at the John Beswick Studios. They failed to capture the collectors imagination and were withdrawn from production at the end of 1985. Even today they are generally not considered to be part of the usual Beatrix Potter collection.

Proving to be more popular is the range of tableware and giftware decorated with Beatrix Potter characters which was introduced in 1987 and is still available today. These were the first Beatrix Potter items to carry the Royal Albert backstamp.

After Royal Doulton transfered the Beatrix Potter figures from the Beswick backstamp to Royal Albert it would have seemed logical that all new issues should carry the Royal Albert mark. In 1993 to celebrate the centenary of Peter Rabbit a new large size version of Peter was issued which for that year only had a special commemorative Beswick backstamp. From 1994 onwards it would become Royal Albert. Peter Rabbit was joined in the Royal Albert range by two further large size figures, Jeremy Fisher and Tom Kitten. It would appear that Royal Doulton became rather fond of centenary celebrations as 1994 saw the hundreth anniversary of the founding of the Beswick company. It was marked by the issue of a large size version of Jemima Puddle Duck which for one year only would carry the Beswick backstamp before changing to Royal Albert. Royal Doulton predicted that 'this special Beswick item will no doubt prove hugely popular amongst collectors and Beatrix Potter lovers alike'. The range of these large size figures eventually extended to ten. Foxy Whiskered Gentleman, Mrs. Rabbit, Tailor of Gloucester, Mrs Tiggy-Winkle, Benjamin Bunny and Peter Rabbit with Handkerchief having been added to the Royal Albert collection. During 1997 and 1998, Lawleys-By-Post issued all ten figures again, in pairs, each with individual numbers and each limited to 1947 pieces. The 'Beswick Ware' backstamp was used and the issue was to commemorate 50 years of making Beatrix Potter figures at the Beswick factory.

To date only the lamp base, the character shaped wall plaques and to some extent the character jugs have shown signs fo catching up the figures in the collectability stakes. No doubt if the enthusiasm for Beatrix Potter's work continues to grow, and there is no reason to suppose it will not, the other items will eventually take off and become highly prized collectables.

When she wrote and illustrated that first letter to Master Moore could Beatrix Potter have imagined what she had created?

How Bunnykins and Beatrix Potter Figures are made

Bunnykins and Beatrix Potter figures are made in the same way at the same factory. Even though they carry different backstamps, Royal Doulton and Beswick or Royal Albert respectively, both ranges are made at Royal Doulton's John Beswick factory at Longton, Stoke-on-Trent.

The one real difference is one of source. All the Beatrix Potter figures are taken from Miss Potter's original illustrations while Bunnykin figures spring from the imaginations of Royal Doulton's team of designers and just occasionally an outside artist.

If it is a Beatrix Potter figure that is to be created the in-house designer will study the original illustration of the character and generally familiarise themselves with the character. He will then produce reference drawings for the modeller, filling in the necessary details to turn a one dimensional illustration into a three dimensional model. In the case of a Bunnykins figure the designer will work from a design brief or perhaps his own ideas. The modeller and the designer work together to produce a clay model of the proposed figure. Assuming that the model is not rejected at this point, a set of plaster of Paris master moulds will be made. How many moulds depends on the complexity of the figure. Usually a Bunnykins figure needs a seven part mould, three for the head and four for the body. The original clay model is cut into pieces to allow the moulding to take place. This is a very skilled job as mistakes cannot easily be rectified. Three or four figures are cast from these moulds for colour trial and approval.

It is undesirable to cast too many figures at this stage. If the model is passed for production, and some are rejected at this stage, the mould has to be used again to make the rubber case from which the working moulds will be made. Over use will result in a blurring of the detail in the figure. With Beatrix Potter figures the trial pieces have to be approved by the copyright holders to ensure that the figure is true to the original illustration.

Once approval is received and the working moulds made, production can commence. Both Bunnykins and Beatrix Potter figures are cast in earthenware in liquid form known as slip. The slip is poured into the assembled mould through a hole in the top. Some of the moisture in the slip is absorbed by the Plaster of Paris moulds and a crust or skin is formed on the inside of the mould. When the required thickness is achieved, the excess slip is poured away and the mould carefully dismantled. The constituent parts are then assembled using more slip to 'glue' them together. The resulting joins are sponged smooth, a process known as fettling. The figure is extremely fragile and it takes great skill not to damage it during handling. After being allowed to dry out the figure is ready for its first firing. The kiln is heated to 1200°C. which dries out any moisture left in the body. This results in a shrinkage of about $\frac{1}{12}$th of the figure's original size. The figure is now at what is known as the biscuit stage and ready for decoration.

Working from an approved completed figure the painters now apply under glaze ceramic colours. The paint is fired on during a second firing at the lower temperature of 760°C. On emerging from the kiln the figure is allowed to cool before being dipped in liquid glaze. It is then fired once more, this time at just over 1000°C. The figure comes out of the kiln in its finished form. Occasionally, when there is a need for special colours some on-glaze colours are added. These too need to be fired on but at a much lower temperature. The red of Santa Bunnykins suit is an example of on-glaze colours being used.

Each completed figure is then inspected for imperfections as Royal Doulton insist that quality control is extremely strict. Then the perfect figures start their journey to collectors around the world . . .

Rarities and Oddities

For some collectors there is always an appeal in having something different or unusual. Over the years there have been many changes in modelling and colouring within the Beatrix Potter figure collection and so there is scope to assemble a collection of unusual pieces. Of course these rarities will carry a price premium. So far, however, the Bunnykins figure collection has remained more or less unchanged with regard to this sort of alteration but as the popularity of the rnage has continued to grow, eagle-eyed collectors have noticed some subtle variants of colour and pose. Consequently the collectability of these non-standard models has increased with the usual associated rise in value.

Bunnykins Figures

With some exceptions the Bunnykins figures which can be considered as rare are those which were, quite simply, produced in limited numbers. The Bunnykins figures introduced in 1939 are scarce because the outbreak of war ended the production of most decorative ceramics. Consequently their production span was very short and over the subsequent years breakages will have reduced their number still more. The same is true of the bunny-shaped tableware introduced at the same time. It is not surprising that pieces bought in 1939 for a few shillings are now worth hundreds, if not thousands, of pounds.

Of the more recent Bunnykins figures it is largely the various limited editions which have become more difficult to find and therefore more expensive. Leading the way is Collector Bunnykins but some of the colourways produced for special events in the United States are also very elusive.

There are only a few colour changes to be considered. Over the years slight variation in the colouring of certain figures has occured but the differences are so slight as to make very little change to the value of the piece. William Bunnykins has been found with an unpainted white jacket which obviously changes his appearance and could increase the value of the figure. A recent change to the colour of the cross on Nurse Bunnykins uniform from red to green has added a premium to figures with the original red colouring. Although if the current version is discontinued, it could be that the green cross variation will be considered rarer than the red.

It is almost unheard of for pilot versions of Bunnykins figures to 'escape' onto the market., although the prototype of Uncle Sam Bunnykins was auctioned for charity in the USA in 1992. This version was almost identical to the standard colouring except his bow tie was yellow rather than red. As only one copy is known in circulation it is interesting for the collector to know that the variation exists, but it does not really form part of the collection proper.

Beatrix Potter Figures

The story is somewhat different with regard to Beatrix Potter figures. At least nineteen figures have been remodelled or recoloured in some way. Some have been changed more than once. Some changes were for technical reasons, and some for practical reasons to make production easier. For example Mrs. Rabbit's umbrella was originally positioned away from her body and therefore vulnerable to being broken off. The figure was remodelled with the umbrella against her skirt. Some of the colour changes are the result of suggestions from the copyright holders of the original books to bring the figure more in line with the illustrations. Other colourings vary due to changes in ceramic paint formulas. On other occasions changes were made simply to make the figure more attractive.

Listed below are the nineteen figures which are known to exist in varying forms. There may be more. The publishers would be pleased to hear from collectors who have found other variations.

1105 Benjamin Bunny
1 Pale green jacket, light green beret with yellow and orange pom-poms. Ears out, shoes out.
2 Brown jacket, dark green beret with orange pom-pom. Ears out, shoes in
3 Tan jacket, green beret with orange pom-pom. Ears in, shoes in.
2803 Benjamin Bunny Sat on a Bank
1 Brown jacket. Head looks down.
2 Golden-brown jacket. Head looks up.
1941 Cecily Parsley
1 Blue dress, white apron, brown pail. Head down.
2 Blue dress, white apron, Head up.
2586 Fierce Bad Rabbit
1 Brown and white rabbit, red-brown carrot, green seat. Feet out.
2 Brown and white rabbit, red-brown carrot, green seat. Feet in.
1104 Little Pig Robinson
1 White and blue striped dress, brown basket with yellow cauliflowers.
2 Blue textured checked dress, brown basket with cream cauliflowers
1275 Miss Moppet
1 Dark brown mottled cat, blue checked kerchief.
2 Light brown striped cat, blue checked kerchief.
1940 Mr Benjamin Bunny
1 Dark maroon jacket, yellow waistcoat. Pipe out.
2 Lilac jacket, yellow waistcoat. Pipe in.
2453 Mr. Jackson
1 Green frog, mauve jacket
2 Brown frog, mauve jacket
1157 Mr. Jeremy Fisher
1 Green frog with small brown spots on head and legs. Lilac coat.
2 Green frog with large spots on head and stripes on legs. Lilac coat.
3 Green frog. Lilac coat.
1200 Mrs Rabbit
1 Pink and yellow striped dress, red collar and cap. Yellow straw coloured basket. Umbrella out.
2 Rose-pink and yellow striped dress, red collar and cap. Light straw coloured basket. Umbrella moulded to dress.
3 White, pink, yellow and green costume.
1107 Mrs. Tiggywinkle
1 Red-brown and white dress, green and blue striped skirt, white apron. The stripes are diagonal.
2 Red-brown and white dress, green and blue striped skirt, white apron. Square stripes.
1098 Peter Rabbit
1 Brown and white rabbit wearing medium blue jacket.
2 Brown and white rabbit wearing light blue jacket.
1365 Pigling Bland
1 Maroon jacket, blue waistcoat, yellow trousers.
2 Lilac jacket, blue waistcoat, yellow trousers.
2452 Sally Henny-Penny
1 Brown and gold chicken. Black hat and cloak, two yellow chicks. Mouth open.
2 Brown and gold chicken. Black hat and cloak, two yellow chicks. Mouth closed.

1102 Squirrel Nutkin
1   Red-brown squirrel holding green-brown nut.
2   Golden-brown squirrel holding green nut

1676 Tabitha Twitchit
1   Blue and white striped dress, white apron, blue striped top.
2   Blue and white striped dress, white apron, white top.

1101 Timmy Tiptoes
1   Grey squirrel with brown shading wearing red jacket.
2   Grey squirrel wearing pink jacket.

1100 Tom Kitten
1   Tabby kitten wearing medium blue trousers and jacket. Dark grren base.
2   Tabby kitten wearing darker blue trousers and jacket. Light green base.

1348 Tommy Brock
1   Blue jacket, pink waistcoat, yellow-green trousers. Small eye patch. Handle of spade out.
2   Blue jacket, red waistcoat, yellow-green trousers. Darker green base. Handle of spade out. Large eye patch.
3   Blue jacket, pink waistcoat, yellow-green trousers. Small eye patch. Handle of spade in.
4   Darker blue jacket, red waistcoat, yellow-green trousers. Large eye-patch. Handle of spade in.

Beatrix Potter Figure Backstamps

The backstamps used on Beatrix Potter figures have changed many times since 1948. Unlike Bunnykins figure backstamps they can be a useful aid in dating a particular piece as the figures did not retain their original mark but as backstamps changed all current production was marked with the new backstamp. Broadly speaking there are three styles of backstamp, Beswick Gold, Beswick Brown and Royal Albert. However the backstamps are a little more complex than this. Illustrated below are the three main types together with descriptions of the variations.

Beswick Gold

1 Circular Beswick mark. Beatrix Potter in upper case type, character's name in italic script, c1948.

2 Oval Beswick mark. Beatrix Potter in upper case type. Character's name in italic script, sometimes within quotation marks. Can occur with 'copyright' in italic script, again c1948.

3 Oval Beswick mark. Beatrix Potter in upper case type. Character's name in upper case type within quotation marks.

An example of Beswick Gold backstamp.

4 Oval Beswick mark. Beatrix Potter and character's name in handwritten style script, c1955.

5 Oval Beswick mark. Beatrix Potter in upper case type, character's name in script. From 1961.

6 Oval Beswick mark. Beatrix Potter in upper case type, character's name in lower case type. Can occur with Beatrix Potter in slanted type. From 1971.

7 Oval Beswick mark. Beatrix Potter in upper case type, character's name in upper case type. 1971-72

Beswick Brown

1 Beswick England. F. Warne & Co. Ltd. Beatrix Potter and the character's name in upper case type. Character name in quotation marks. Copyright date included. 1972

2 Beswick England. Beatrix Potter in upper case type. F. Warne & Co. Ltd and character's name in lower case type. Character's name in quotation marks. Copyright date included. 1974.

3 Beswick Made in England. Beatrix Potter in upper case type. F. Warne & Co. Ltd and character's name in lower case type. Character's name in quotation marks. Copyright date included. 1973.

4   Beswick England. Beatrix Potter in upper case type. F. Warne & Co. Ltd and character's name in lower case type. Copyright date included. 1974.

5   Beswick England. Beatrix Potter in upper case type. Frederick Warne PLC and character's name in lower case type. Character's name in quotation marks. Copyright date included. 1982.

6   Beswick England. Beatrix Potter (no's) in upper case type. Character's name in lower case type with quotation marks. F. Warne & Co. in lower case. Licensed by Copyrights added. 1984.

An example of Beswick Brown backstamp.

7   Beswick England. Beatrix Potter (no's) in upper case type. Character's name in lower case type with quotation marks. Frederick Warne & Co. in lower case. Licensed by Copyrights added. 1985.

8   John Beswick script mark. Beatrix Potter in upper case type. Character's name in lower case type with quotation marks. F. Warne & Co. and licensed by Copyrights in lower case type. John Beswick in script. Studio of Royal Doulton in lower case type. 1988.

9   John Beswick script mark. Beatrix Potter in upper case type. Character's name in lower case type with quotation marks. Frederick Warne & Co. and licensed by Copyrights in lower case type. John Beswick in script. Studio of Royal Doulton in lower case type. 1988.

BESWICK
MADE IN ENGLAND
Old Mr Brown
Beatrix Potter
© F. WARNE & CO. 1963
© 1989 ROYAL DOULTON

BESWICK
MADE IN ENGLAND
Mrs Rabbit
Beatrix Potter
© F. WARNE & CO. 1951
© 1989 ROYAL DOULTON

BESWICK
MADE IN ENGLAND
Mrs Rabbit cooking
Beatrix Potter
© F. WARNE & CO. 1991
© 1992 ROYAL DOULTON

The three backstamps above are examples of the types of backstamps to be found on the latest Beswick Beatrix Potter figures.

1851 *Anna Maria* modelled by Albert Hallam. Introduced 1963, withdrawn 1983.

2061 *Amiable Guinea Pig* modelled by Albert Hallam. Introduced 1967, withdrawn 1983.

3319 *And This Little Pig Had None* modelled by Martyn Alcock. Royal Albert backstamp, introduced 1992 and was withdrawn in 1998.

2333 *Appley Dapply* modelled by Albert Hallam. Introduced in 1971, still current.

2276 *Aunt Pettitoes* modelled by Albert Hallam. Introduced 1970, withdrawn 1993.

2971 *Babbitty Bumble* modelled by Warren Platt. Royal Albert backstamp. Introduced 1989, withdrawn 1993.

3317 *Benjamin Ate A Lettuce Leaf* modelled by Martyn Alcock. Introduced 1992, withdrawn 1998

1105 *Benjamin Bunny* modelled by Arthur Greddington. Three versions. Introduced in 1948, still current.

3403 large size *Benjamin Bunny* modelled by Martyn Alcock. Introduced 1994, withdrawn 1997.

2803 *Benjamin Bunny Sat On A Bank* modelled by David Lyttleton. Introduced 1983, withdrawn 1997.

3234 *Benjamin Wakes Up* modelled by Amanda Hughes-Lubeck. Introduced in 1991, withdrawn 1997.

1941 *Cecily Parsley* modelled by Arthur Gredington Introduced 1964, withdrawn 1993.

2627 *Chippy Hackee* modelled by David Lyttleton. Introduced 1979, withdrawn 1993.

3257 *Christmas Stocking* modelled by Martyn Alcock. Introduced 1991, withdrawn 1994

2713 *Diggory Diggory Delvet* modelled by David Lyttleton. Introduced in 1982 withdrawn 1997.

2878 *Cottontail* modelled by David Lyttleton. Introduced in 1985, withdrawn 1996.

2284 *Cousin Ribby* modelled by Albert Hallam. Introduced 1970, withdrawn 1993.

1355 *Duchess (with flowers)* modelled by Graham Orwell, Introduced in 1955 withdrawn 1967.

2601 *Duchess (with pie)* modelled by Graham Tongue, Introduced 1979, withdrawn 1982.

2586 *Fierce Bad Rabbit* modelled by David Lyttleton. Introduced in 1977, withdrawn 1997.

1277 *Foxy Whiskered Gentleman* modelled by Arthur Gredington. Introduced 1953, still current.

3450 Large *Foxy Whiskered Gentleman* modelled by Amanda Hughes-Lubeck. Introduced 1995, withdrawn 1997.

1274 *Floppy Mopsy & Cottontail* modelled by Arthur Gredington. Introduced January 1953, withdrawn 1997.

3219*Foxy Reading Country News* modelled by Amanda Hughes-Lubeck. Introduced 1990, withdrawn 1997.

1675 *Goody Tiptoes* modelled by Arthur Gredington. Introduced in 1960, withdrawn 1997.

Right: 2957 *Goody and Timmy Tiptoes*, modelled by David Lyttleton. Introduced 1986, withdrawn 1996.

Left: 2559 *Ginger* modelled by David Lyttleton. Introduced 1976, withdrawn 1982.

3766 *Hiding From The Cat* modelled by Graham Tongue. Issued in 1988 for one year only.

1198 *Hunca Munca* modelled by Arthur Gredington, Introduced May 1951, still current.

3288 *Hunca Munca Spills the Beans* modelled by Martyn Alcock. Introduced 1992, withdrawn 1996.

2584 *Hunca Munca Sweeping* modelled by David Lyttleton, Introduced 1977, still current.

1092 *Jemina Puddle Duck* modelled by Arthur Gredington. Introduced 1947 still current.

3373 *Jemima Puddle Duck* large size, modelled by Martyn Alcock. Introduced 1994, discontinued 1997.

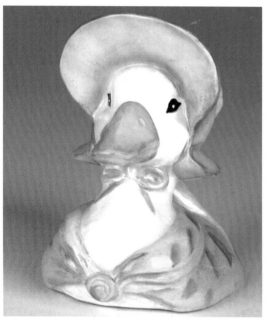

3088 *Jemina Puddle Duck* Character Jug. Introduced 1988, withdrawn 1992.

3193 *Jemina Puddle Duck with Foxy Whiskered Gentleman* modelled by Ted Chawner. Introduced 1990, still current.

3786 *Jemina Puddle Duck and Ducklings* modelled by Martyn Alcock. Introduced 1998, still current.

2823 *Jemina Puddle Duck Made a Feather Nest* modelled by David Lyttleton. Introduced 1984, withdrawn 1997.

Jemima Puddle Duck Money Box. Modeller, not known, Royal Albert backstamp. Introduced in 1992, still current.

2082 *Jemina Puddle Duck* wall figural modelled by Albert Hallam. Introduced 1967, withdrawn 1969.

Right: 1276 *Johnny Townmouse* modelled by Arthur Gredington. Introduced 1953, withdrawn 1993.

3094 *Johnny Townmouse With Bag* modelled by Ted Chawner. Introduced, 1988, withdrawn 1994.

Left: 2965 *John Joiner* modelled by Graham Tongue, under Royal Albert backstamp. Introduced 1990, withdrawn 1997.

Right: 1183 *Lady Mouse* modelled by Arthur Gredington. Introduced 1950, still current.

2585 *Little Black Rabbit* modelled by David Lyttleton. Introduced 1977, withdrawn 1997.

1104 *Little Pig Robinson* modelled by Arthur Gredington. Introduced 1948, still current.

3031 *Little Pig Robinson, Spying* modelled by Ted Chawner introduced in 1987, withdrawn 1993.

Front and rear view of 3251 *Miss Dormouse* modelled by Martyn Alcock. Under Royal Albert backstamp. Introduced 1991, withdrawn 1995.

1275 *Miss Moppet* modelled by Arthur Gredington. Introduced 1953, still current.

3197 *Mittens and Moppet* modelled by Ted Chawner. Introduced 1990, withdrawn 1994.

2966 *Mother Ladybird* modelled by Warren Platt. Introduced 1989, withdrawn 1996.

2424 *Mr Alderman Ptolemy* modelled by Graham Tongue, introduced 1973, withdrawn 1997.

2509 *Mr. Benjamin Bunny and Peter Rabbit* modelled by Alan Maslankowski. Introduced 1974, withdrawn 1995.

1940 *Mr Benjamin Bunny* modelled by Arthur Gredington introduced 1964, still current.

2628 *Mr. Drake Puddle Duck* modelled by David Lyttleton. Introduced 1979, still current.

2453 *Mr Jackson* modelled by Albert Hallam. Introduced 1973, withdrawn 1997.

1157 *Mr Jeremy Fisher* modelled by Arthur Gredington. Introduced 1950, still current.

3372 large size *Jeremy Fisher* modelled by Martyn Alcock. Introduced 1994, withdrawn 1997.

2960 *Jeremy Fisher* Character jug. Introduced 1987, withdrawn 1992.

3090 *Mr Jeremy Fisher Digging* modelled by Ted Chawner, introduced 1988. Withdrawn 1994

3091 *Mr Tod* modelled by Ted Chawner. Introduced 1988, withdrawn 1993.

3506 *Mr. McGregor* modelled by Martyn Alcock. Introduced 1995, still current.

1942 *Mrs Flopsy Bunny* modelled by Arthur Gredington. Introduced 1964, withdrawn 1998.

3398 large size *Mrs Rabbit* modelled by Martyn Alcock. Introduced 1994, withdrawn 1997.

1200 *Mrs Rabbit* modelled by Arthur Gredington. There are two versions. The early one has the umbrella separate from the main figure, the later has the umbrella moulded onto the main model body. Introduced 1951, still current.

3278 *Mrs Rabbit Cooking* modelled by Martyn Alcock. Introduced 1992, still current.

2543 *Mrs Rabbit and Bunnies* modelled by David Lyttleton. Introduced 1976, withdrawn 1997.

3646 *Mrs Rabbit and Peter* modelled by Warren Platt. Introduced 1997 and still current.

This special piece depicting 3672 *Mrs Rabbit and the Four Bunnies* has been produced in 1997 to commemorate the fifieth anniversary of the introduction of Beatrix Potter characters by John Beswick in 1947. It is the first Beatrix Potter tableau scene to be produced and has a special Beswick backstamp. The model is on a wooden plinth and features Mrs Rabbit, Flopsy, Mopsy, Cotton Tail and Peter Rabbit and is in a limited edition of 1997.

3102 *Mrs Tiggywinkle* character jug, modelled by Ted Chawner. Introduced 1988, withdrawn 1992.

3789 *Mrs Tiggywinkle Washing* modelled by Warren Platt, introduced 1998, still current.

Mrs Tiggywinkle top: 1107 modelled by Arthur Gredington, introduced 1948, still current. Bottom: 3437 large size by Martyn Alcock, introduced 1997 for one year only.

2877 *Mrs Tiggywinkle Takes Tea* modelled by David Lyttleton. Introduced 1985, still current.

1103 *Mrs Tittlemouse* modelled by Arthur Gredington. Introduced 1948, withdrawn 1993.

3325 *No More Twist* modelled by Martyn Alcock. Introduced 1992, withdrawn 1997.

Right: 2956 *Old Mr Bouncer* modelled by David Lyttleton. Introduced 1986, discontinued 1995.

1796 *Old Mr. Brown* modelled by Albert Hallam. Introduced 1962, still current.

2959 *Old Mr. Brown* Character Jug. Introduced 1987, withdrawn 1992.

2767 *Old Mr. Pricklepin* modelled by David Lyttleton. Introduced 1983, withdrawn 1989.

1098 *Peter Rabbit* modelled by Arthur Gredington. Introduced 1947, still current.

3356 *Peter Rabbit* Introduced 1993, withdrawn 1997.

3533 *Peter Ate a Radish* modelled by Warren Platt. Introduced 1995, still current.

3157 *Peter Rabbit in a Gooseberry Net* modelled by David Lyttleton. Introduced in 1990, discontinued 1995.

3242 *Peter and the Red Pocket Handkerchief* modelled by Martyn Alcock. Introduced 1991, still current.

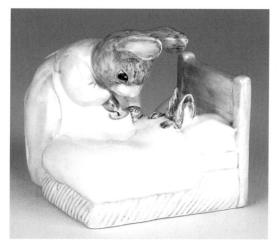

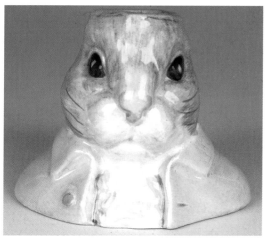

3473 *Peter in Bed* modelled by Martyn Alcock, introduced in 1995, still current.

3006 *Peter Rabbit* Character jug. Introduced 1987, withdrawn 1992.

3739 *Peter Rabbit Gardening* modelled by Warren Platt. Introduced 1998, still current.

3592 *Peter Rabbit with Handkerchief* modelled by Amanda Hughes-Lubeck. Introduced 1996, withdrawn 1997

3391 *Peter Rabbit with Postbag* modelled by Amanda Hughes-Lubeck. Introduced 1996, still current.

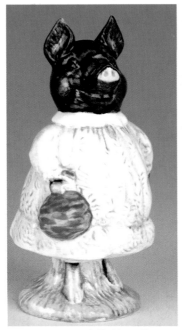

2381 *Pig Wig* modelled by Albert Hallam. Introduced 1971, withdrawn 1982.

1365 *Pigling Bland* modelled by Graham Orwell. Introduced 1955, withdrawn 1998.

3252 *Pigling Eats His Porridge* modelled by Martyn Alcock. Introduced 1991, withdrawn 1994.

2647 *Rebecca Puddle Duck* modelled by David Lyttleton. Introduced 1981, still current.

2334 *Pickles* modelled by Albert Hallam. Introduced 1971, withdrawn 1982.

2560 *Poorly Peter Rabbit* modelled by David Lyttleton. Introduced in 1976, withdrawn 1997.

1199 *Ribby* modelled by Arthur Gredington. Original was called *Ribby* but more recent price lists show *Mrs Ribby*. Introduced 1951, still current.

3280 *Ribby and the Patty Pan* modelled by Martyn Alcock. Introduced 1992, still current.

2452 *Sally Henny Penny* modelled by Albert Hallam. Two versions: early version has open beak, later version has closed beak. Introduced 1973, discontinued 1993.

1106 *Samuel Whiskers* modelled by Arthur Gredington. Various backstamps. First introduced in 1948 and withdrawn in 1995.

2508 *Simpkin* modelled by Alan Maslankowski. Introduced 1974, withdrawn 1982.

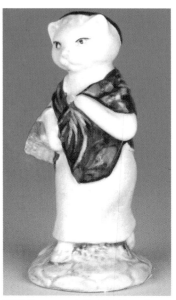

2425 *Sir Isaac Newton* modelled by Graham Tongue. Introduced 1973, withdrawn 1984.

2716 *Susan* modelled by David Lyttleton. This is a very rare model having been made only for four months in 1989 with the Royal Albert backstamp following its take over from the Beswick backstamp.

2716 *Susan* modelled by David Lyttleton, Introduced 1983, withdrawn 1989.

1102 *Squirrel Nutkin* modelled by Arthur Gredington. Early figures had the nut coloured brown whilst later ones it was coloured green. First introduced in 1948 and is still current.

1676 *Tabitha Twitchit* modelled by Arthur Gredington. Introduced 1960, withdrawn 1995.

1108 *Tailor of Gloucester* modelled by Arthur Gredington. Introduced 1948, still current.

3449 large size *Tailor of Gloucester,* modelled by Warren Platt, introduced 1995, withdrawn 1997.

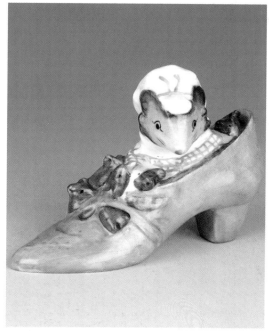

2544 *Tabitha Twitchit and Miss Moppet* modelled by David Lyttleton. Introduced in 1976, withdrawn 1993.

1545 *The Old Woman who lived in a Shoe* modelled by Colin Melbourne. Introduced 1958, withdrawn 1997.

2804 *The Old Woman Who Lived in a Shoe Knitting* modelled by David Lyttleton. Introduced 1983, still current.

2668 *Thomasina Tittlemouse* modelled by David Lyttleton Introduced 1981, withdrawn 1989.

1101 *Timmy Tiptoes* modelled by Arthur Gredington. Introduced 1948, withdrawn 1997.

1109 *Timmy Willie* modelled by Arthur Gredington. Introduced 1948, withdrawn 1993.

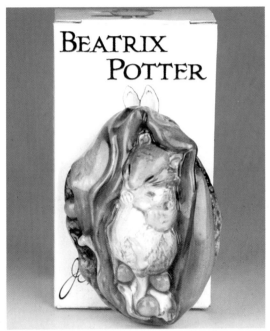

2996 *Timmy Willie Sleeping* modelled by Graham Tongue. Introduced 1987, withdrawn 1996.

3391 *Tom Kittten* modelled by Arthur Gredington, introduced 1947, still current.

3405 large size *Tom Kittten* introduced 1994, withdrawn 1997

3103 *Tom Kitten* character jug modelled by Ted Chawner. Introduced 1988, withdrawn 1992.

2085 *Tom Kitten* plaque modelled by Graham Tongue, introduced 1967, withdrawn 1969.

3030 *Tom Kitten and Butterfly,* modelled by Ted Chawner. Introduced 1987, withdrawn 1994.

3719 *Tom Kitten in the Rockery* modelled by Warren Platt, introduced 1988, still current

2989 *Tom Thumb* modelled by Warren Platt. Introduced in 1988, withdrawn 1998.

1348 *Tommy Brock* modelled by Graham Orwell. Introduced 1955, still current.

Beatrix Potter Listings and Values

Shape No	Version	Production Period	Height	Backstamp	Market Value	

Amiable Guinea Pig™ Modeller Albert Hallam   *picture page 73*

| 2061 | 1 | 1967-1971 | 3½" | Gold | £250-£300 | $415-$495 |
| 2061 | 1 | 1972-1983 | 3½" | Brown | £200-£250 | $330-$415 |

And This Little Pig Had None™ Modeller Martyn Alcock   *picture page 73*

| 3319 | 1 | 1992-1998 | 4" | RA | £30-£35 | $50-$60 |

Anna Maria™ Modeller Albert Hallam   *picture page 73*

| 1851 | 1 | 1963-1971 | 3" | Gold | £175-£200 | $290-$330 |
| 1851 | 1 | 1972-1983 | 3" | Brown | £100-£125 | $165-$205 |

Appley Dapply™ Modeller Albert Hallam   *picture page 73*

2333	1	1971 only	3¼"	Gold	£300-£350	$495-$575
2333	1	1972-1974	3¼"	Gold	£200-£250	$330-$415
2333	2	1974-1989	3¼"	Brown	£30-£35	$50-$60
2333	2	1989-Cur	3¼"	RA	£16	

Aunt Pettitoes™ Modeller Albert Hallam   *picture page 73*

2276	1	1970-1971	3¾"	Gold	£150-£175	$250-$290
2276	1	1972-1989	3¾"	Brown	£40-£50	$65-$85
2276	1	1989-1993	3¾"	RA	£30-£35	$50-$60

Babbitty Bumble™ Modeller Warren Platt   *picture page 73*

| 2971 | 1 | 1989-1993 | 2¾" | RA | £75-£95 | $125-$155 |

Benjamin Ate A Lettuce Leaf™ Modeller Martyn Alcock   *picture page 74*

| 3317 | 1 | 1992-1998 | 4¾" | RA | £30-£35 | $50-$60 |

Benjamin Bunny™ Modeller Arthur Gredington   *picture page 74*

1105	1	1948-1971	4"	Gold	£250-£300	$415-$495
1105	2	1972-1983	4"	Gold	£150-£200	$250-$330
1105	3	1983-1989	4"	Brown	£40-£50	$65-$85
1105	3	1989-Cur	4"	RA	£16	

Benjamin Bunny™ Modeller Martyn Alcock   *picture page 74*

| 3403 | 4 | 1994 | 6¼" | RA | £30-£40 | $50-$65 |

Benjamin Bunny Sat On A Bank™ Modeller David Lyttleton   *picture page 74*

2803	1	1983-1986	3¾"	Brown	£70-£80	$115-$130
2803	2	1986-1989	3¾"	Brown	£40-£50	$65-$85
2803	2	1989-1997	3¾"	RA	£30-£35	$50-$60

Shape No	Version	Production Period	Height	Backstamp	Market Value	

Benjamin Wakes Up™ Modeller Amanda Hughes-Lubeck   *picture page 74*

| 3234 | 1 | 1991-1997 | 2¼" | RA | £30-£35 | $50-$60 |

Cecily Parsley™ Modeller Arthur Gredington   *picture page 75*

1941	1	1964-1971	4"	Gold	£100-£125	$165-$205
1941	2	1972-1984	4"	Brown	£40-£50	$65-$85
1941	2	1989-1993	4"	RA	£30-£35	$50-$60

Chippy Hackee™ Modeller David Lyttleton   *picture page 75*

| 2627 | 1 | 1979-1989 | 3¾" | Brown | £40-£50 | $65-$85 |
| 2627 | 1 | 1989-1993 | 3¾" | RA | £30-£35 | $50-$60 |

Christmas Stocking™ Modeller Martyn Alcock   *picture page 75*

| 3257 | 1 | 1991-1994 | 3¼" | RA | £60-£80 | $100-$130 |

Cottontail™ Modeller David Lyttleton   *picture page 75*

| 2878 | 1 | 1985-1989 | 3¾" | Brown | £40-£50 | $65-$85 |
| 2878 | 1 | 1989-1996 | 3¾" | RA | £30-£35 | $50-$60 |

Cousin Ribby™ Modeller Albert Hallam   *picture page 75*

2284	1	1970-1971	3½"	Gold	£150-£175	$250-$290
2284	1	1972-1989	3½"	Brown	£40-£50	$65-$85
2284	1	1989-1993	3½"	RA	£30-£35	$50-$60

Diggory Diggory Delvet™ Modeller David Lyttleton   *picture page 75*

| 2713 | 1 | 1982-1989 | 2¾" | Brown | £40-£50 | $65-$85 |
| 2713 | 1 | 1989-1997 | 2¾" | RA | £30-£35 | $50-$60 |

Display Stand™ Modeller Andrew Brindley

| 2295 | 1 | 1970-1989 | 12½" | Brown | £30-£40 | $50-$65 |
| 2295 | 1 | 1989-1997 | 12½" | Doulton | £20-£30 | $35-$50 |

Duchess (with Flowers)™ Modeller Graham Orwell   *picture page 75*

| 1355 | 1 | 1955-1967 | 3¾" | Gold | £1500-£1750 | $2475-$2890 |

Duchess (with Pie)™ Modeller Graham Tongue   *picture page 76*

| 2601 | 2 | 1979-1982 | 4" | Brown | £200-£225 | $330-$370 |

Fierce Bad Rabbit™ Modeller David Lyttleton   *picture page 76*

2586	1	1977-1980	4¾"	Brown	£150-£175	$250-$290
2586	2	1980-1989	4¾"	Brown	£40-£50	$65-$85
2586	2	1989-1997	4¾"	RA	£30-£35	$50-$60

Shape No	Version	Production Period	Height	Backstamp	Market Value	

Flopsy, Mopsy and Cottontail™ Modeller Arthur Gredington   *picture page 76*

Shape No	Version	Production Period	Height	Backstamp	Market Value	
1274	1	1953-1971	2½"	Gold	£75-£100	$125-$165
1274	1	1972-1983	2½"	Brown	£50-£75	$85-$125
1274	2	1983-1989	2½"	Brown	£40-£50	$65-$85
1274	2	1989-1997	2½"	RA	£30-£35	$50-$60

Foxy Reading Country News™ Modeller Amanda Hughes-Lubeck   *picture page 77*

Shape No	Version	Production Period	Height	Backstamp	Market Value	
3219	1	1990-1997	4¼"	RA	£40-£60	$65-$100

Foxy Whiskered Gentleman™ Modeller Arthur Gredington   *picture page 76*

Shape No	Version	Production Period	Height	Backstamp	Market Value	
1277	1	1953-1971	4¾"	Gold	£70-£80	$115-$130
1277	1	1972-1989	4¾"	Brown	£40-£50	$65-$85
1277	1	1989-Cur	4¾"	RA	£16	

Foxy Whiskered Gentleman™ Modeller Amanda Hughes-Lubeck   *picture page 76*

Shape No	Version	Production Period	Height	Backstamp	Market Value	
3450	1	1995-1997	7"	RA	£30-£35	$50-$60

Gentleman Mouse Made A Bow™ Modeller Ted Chawner

Shape No	Version	Production Period	Height	Backstamp	Market Value	
3200	1	1990-1996	3"	RA	£30-£35	$50-$60

Ginger™ Modeller David Lyttleton   *picture page 77*

Shape No	Version	Production Period	Height	Backstamp	Market Value	
2559	1	1976-1982	3¾"	Brown	£300-£350	$495-$575

Ginger and Pickles™ (Tableau) Modeller Graham Tongue

Shape No	Version	Production Period	Height	Backstamp	Market Value	
3790	1	1988 only		Spec Bes	£95	$155

Goody and Timmy Tiptoes™ Modeller David Lyttleton   *picture page 77*

Shape No	Version	Production Period	Height	Backstamp	Market Value	
2957	1	1986-1989	4"	Brown	£100-£125	$165-$205
2957	1	1989-1996	4"	RA	£40-£50	$65-$85

Goody Tiptoes™ Modeller Arthur Gredington   *picture page 77*

Shape No	Version	Production Period	Height	Backstamp	Market Value	
1675	1	1960-1971	3½"	Gold	£70-£80	$115-$130
1675	1	1972-1989	3½"	Brown	£40-£50	$65-$85
1675	1	1989-1997	3½"	RA	£30-£35	$50-$60

Hiding from the Cat™ (Tableau) Modeller Graham Tongue   *picture page 78*

Shape No	Version	Production Period	Height	Backstamp	Market Value	
3766	1	1988 only		Spec Bes	£100	$165

Hunca Munca™ Modeller Arthur Gredington   *picture page 78*

Shape No	Version	Production Period	Height	Backstamp	Market Value	
1198	1	1951-1971	2¾"	Gold	£70-£80	$115-$130
1198	1	1972-1989	2¾"	Brown	£40-£50	$65-$85
1198	1	1989-Cur	2¾"	RA	£16	

Shape No	Version	Production Period	Height	Backstamp	Market Value	

Hunca Munca Spills The Beans™ Modeller Martyn Alcock
picture page 78

| 3288 | 1 | 1992-1996 | 3¼″ | RA | £30-£35 | $50-$60 |

Hunca Munca Sweeping™ Modeller David Lyttleton
picture page 78

2584	1	1977-1989	3½″	Brown	£40-£50	$65-$85
2584	1	1989-Cur	3½″	RA	£16	
2584¹	1	1998	3½″		£25	

¹Gold edition only available for 6 months

Jemima Puddle Duck™ Modeller Arthur Gredington
picture page 78

1092	1	1947-1971	4¾″	Gold	£70-£80	$115-$130
1092	1	1971-1983	4¾″	Brown	£40-£50	$65-$85
1092	2	1983-1989	4¾″	Brown	£30-£35	$50-$60
1092	2	1989-Cur	4¾″	RA	£16	
1092¹	2	1997	4¾″	Bes	£25	

¹Gold edition

Jemima Puddle Duck™ Modeller Martyn Alcock
picture page 79

| 3373 | 1 | 1994-1997 | 6″ | RA | £30-£35 | $50-$60 |
| 3373¹ | 1 | 1998 | 6″ | | £25 | |

¹Gold edition, limited edition 1947

Jemima Puddle Duck and Ducklings™ Modeller Martyn Alcock
picture page 79

| 3786 | 1 | 1998-Cur | | New Bes £28 | | |

Jemima Puddle Duck with Foxy Whiskered Gentleman™
Modeller Ted Chawner
picture page 79

| 3193 | 1 | 1990-Cur | 4¾″ | RA | £28 | |

Jemima Puddle Duck & Foxy Whiskered Gentleman™ (Wall Plaque)
Modellers Harry Sales & David Lyttleton

| 2594 | 1 | 1977-1982 | 7½″ | Brown | £80-£100 | $130-$165 |

Jemima Puddle Duck™ (character jug) Modeller Ted Chawner
picture page 79

| 3088 | 1 | 1988-1989 | 4″ | Brown | £100-£125 | $165-$205 |
| 3088 | 1 | 1989-1992 | 4″ | RA | £75-£100 | $125-$165 |

Jemima Puddle Duck Made A Feathered Nest™
Modeller David Lyttleton
picture page 80

| 2823 | 1 | 1984-1989 | 2¼″ | Brown | £40-£50 | $65-$85 |
| 2823 | 1 | 1989-1997 | 2¼″ | RA | £30-£35 | $50-$60 |

Shape No	Version	Production Period	Height	Backstamp	Market Value	

Jemima Puddle Duck™ (money box) Modeller Unknown
picture page 80

	1	1992-Cur		RA	£12	

Jemima Puddle Duck™ (wall figural) Modeller Albert Hallam
picture page 80

2082	1	1967-1969	6″	Gold	£1500-£2000	$2475-$3300

John Joiner™ Modeller Graham Tongue
picture page 80

2965	1	1990-1997	2½″	RA	£30-£35	$50-$60

Johnny Townmouse™ Modeller Arthur Gredington
picture page 80

1276	1	1953-1971	3½″	Gold	£70-£80	$115-$130
1276	1	1971-1989	3½″	Brown	£40-£50	$65-$85
1276	1	1989-1993	3½″	RA	£30-£35	$50-$60

Johnny Townmouse With Bag™ Modeller Ted Chawner
picture page 80

3094	1	1988-1989	3½″	Brown	£125-£150	$205-$250
3094	1	1989-1994	3½″	RA	£75-£100	$125-$165

Lady Mouse™ Modeller Arthur Gredington
picture page 80

1183	1	1950-1971	4″	Gold	£75-£100	$125-$165
1183	1	1971-1989	4″	Brown	£40-£50	$65-$85
1183	1	1989-Cur	4″	RA	£16	

Lady Mouse Made A Curtsey™ Modeller Amanda Hughes-Lubeck

3220	1	1990-1997	3¼″	RA	£30-£35	$50-$60

Little Black Rabbit™ Modeller David Lyttleton
picture page 81

2585	1	1977-1989	4½″	Brown	£40-£50	$65-$85
2585	1	1989-1997	4½″	RA	£30-£35	$50-$60

Little Pig Robinson™ Modeller Arthur Gredington
picture page 81

1104	1	1948-1971	4″	Gold	£80-£100	$130-$165
1104	1	1971-1974	3½″	Brown	£70-£80	$115-$130
1104	2	1974-1989	3½″	Brown	£30-£35	$50-$60
1104	2	1989-Cur	3½″	RA	£16	

Little Pig Robinson Spying™ Modeller Ted Chawner
picture page 81

3031	1	1987-1989	3½″	Brown	£150-£175	$250-$290
3031	1	1989-1993	3½″	RA	£75-£100	$125-$165

Miss Dormouse™ Modeller Martyn Alcock
picture page 81

3251	1	1991-1995	4″	RA	£50-£75	$85-$125

Shape No	Version	Production Period	Height	Backstamp	Market Value	

Miss Moppet™ Modeller Arthur Gredington *picture page 81*

1275	1	1953-1971	3″	Gold	£70-£80	$115-$130
1275	2	1971-1989	3″	Brown	£40-£50	$65-$85
1275	2	1989-Cur	3″	RA	£16	

Mittens and Moppet™ Modeller Ted Chawner *picture page 82*

| 3197 | 1 | 1990-1994 | 3¾″ | RA | £75-£100 | $125-$165 |

Mittens, Tom Kitten and Moppet™ (Tableau) Modeller Amanda Hughes-Lubeck

| 3792 | 1 | 1999-Cur | | Spec Bes | £100 | |

Mother Ladybird™ Modeller Warren Platt *picture page 82*

| 2966 | 1 | 1989-1996 | 2½″ | RA | £30-£35 | $50-$60 |

Mr Alderman Ptolemy™ Modeller Graham Tongue *picture page 82*

| 2424 | 1 | 1973-1989 | 3½″ | Brown | £50-£75 | $85-$125 |
| 2424 | 1 | 1989-1997 | 3½″ | RA | £30-£35 | $50-$60 |

Mr Benjamin Bunny™ Modeller Arthur Gredington *picture page 83*

1940	1	1964-1971	4¼″	Gold	£250-£300	$415-$495
1940	1	1971-1974	4¼″	Brown	£200-£250	$330-$415
1940	2	1974-1989	4½″	Brown	£30-£35	$50-$60
1940	2	1989-Cur	4½″	RA	£16	

Mr Benjamin Bunny and Peter Rabbit™
Modeller Alan Maslankowski *picture page 82*

| 2509 | 1 | 1974-1989 | 4″ | Brown | £75-£100 | $125-$165 |
| 2509 | 1 | 1989-1995 | 4″ | RA | £40-£50 | $65-$85 |

Mr Drake Puddleduck™ Modeller David Lyttleton *picture page 83*

| 2628 | 1 | 1979-1989 | 4″ | Brown | £40-£50 | $65-$85 |
| 2628 | 1 | 1989-Cur | 4″ | RA | £16 | |

Mr Jackson™ Modeller Albert Hallam *picture page 83*

2453	1	1973-1976	2¾″	Brown	£150-£200	$250-$330
2453	2	1977-1989	2¾″	Brown	£40-£50	$65-$85
2453	2	1989-1997	2¾″	RA	£30-£35	$50-$60

Mr Jeremy Fisher™ Modeller Arthur Gredington *picture page 83*

1157	1	1950-1971	3″	Gold	£100-£125	$165-$205
1157	1	1972-1983	3″	Brown	£75-£100	$125-$165
1157	2	1983-1989	3″	Brown	£40-£50	$65-$85
1157	2	1989-Cur	3″	RA	£16	

Shape No	Version	Production Period	Height	Backstamp	Market Value	

Mr Jeremy Fisher™ Modeller Martyn Alcock   *picture page 83*

3372	3	1994-1997	5″	RA	£30-£35	$50-$60

Mr Jeremy Fisher™ (character jug) Modeller Graham Tongue   *picture page 84*

2960	4	1987-1989	3″	Brown	£100-£125	$165-$205
2960	4	1989-1992	3″	RA	£75-£100	$125-$165

Mr Jeremy Fisher Digging™ Modeller Ted Chawner   *picture page 84*

3090	1	1988-1989	3¾″	Brown	£150-£175	$250-$290
3090	1	1989-1994	3¾″	RA	£75-£100	$125-$165

Mr McGregor™ Modeller Martyn Alcock   *picture page 84*

3506	1	1995-Cur	5¼″	RA	£28	

Mr Tod™ Modeller Ted Chawner   *picture page 84*

3091	1	1988-1989	4¾″	Brown	£150-£175	$250-$290
3091	1	1989-1993	4¾″	RA	£75-£100	$125-$165

Mrs Flopsy Bunny™ Modeller Arthur Gredington   *picture page 85*

1942	1	1964-1971	4″	Gold	£100-£125	$165-$205
1942	1	1971-1989	4″	Brown	£40-£50	$65-$85
1942	1	1989-1998	4″	RA	£30-£35	$50-$60

Mrs Rabbit™ Modeller Arthur Gredington   *picture page 85*

1200	1	1951-1971	4¼″	Gold	£200-£250	$330-$415
1200	1	1971-1974	4¼″	Brown	£175-£200	$290-$330
1200	2	1974-1989	4¼″	Brown	£40-£50	$65-$85
1200	2	1989-Cur	4¼″	RA	£16	

Mrs Rabbit™ Modeller Martyn Alcock   *picture page 85*

3398	1	1994-1997	6″	RA	£30-£35	$50-$60

Mrs Rabbit and Bunnies™ Modeller David Lyttleton   *picture page 85*

2543	1	1976-1989	3¾″	Brown	£40-£50	$65-$85
2543	1	1989-1997	3¾″	RA	£30-£35	$50-$60

Mrs Rabbit and Peter Modeller Warren Platt   *picture page 85*

3646	1	1997-Cur	3½″	RA	£28	

Mrs Rabbit and the Four Bunnies (Tableau) Modeller Shane Ridge   *picture page 86*

3672	1	1997 only	4¼″	Special	£300-£400	$495-$660

Shape No	Version	Production Period	Height	Backstamp	Market Value	

Mrs Rabbit Cooking™ Modeller Martyn Alcock   *picture page 85*

3278	1	1992-Cur	4″	RA	£16	

Mrs Tiggywinkle™ Modeller Arthur Gredingon   *picture page 86*

1107	1	1948-1971	3¼″	Gold	£100-£125	$165-$205
1107	1	1972-1975	3¼″	Brown	£75-£100	$125-$165
1107	2	1975-1989	3¼″	Brown	£40-£50	$65-$85
1107	2	1989-Cur	3¼″	RA	£16	
1107[1]	2	1998	3¼″		£25	

[1]Gold edition - available for 6 months only

Mrs Tiggywinkle™ Modeller Martyn Alcock   *picture page 86*

3437	1	1997 only	4½″	RA	£40-£50	$65-$85
3437[1]	1	1998	4½″		£25	

[1]Gold edition – limited edition 1947

Mrs Tiggywinkle Washing™ Modeller Warren Platt   *picture page 86*

3789	1	1998-cur		New Bes	£16	

Mrs Tiggywinkle™ (character jug) Modeller Ted Chawner   *picture page 86*

3102	1	1988-1989	3″	Brown	£100-£125	$165-$205
3102	1	1989-1992	3″	RA	£75-£100	$125-$165

Mrs Tiggywinkle Takes Tea™ Modeller David Lyttleton   *picture page 86*

2877	1	1985-1989	3¼″	Brown	£100-£125	$165-$205
2877	1	1989-Cur	3¼″	RA	£16	

Mrs Tittlemouse™ Modeller Athur Gredington   *picture page 87*

1103	1	1948-1971	3½″	Gold	£100-£125	$165-$205
1103	1	1971-1989	3½″	Brown	£40-£50	$65-$85
1103	1	1989-1993	3½″	RA	£30-£35	$50-$60

Mrs Tittlemouse™ (plaque) Modeller Harry Sales

2685	1	1981-1982	7½″	Brown	£150-£175	$250-$290

No More Twist™ Modeller Martyn Alcock   *picture page 87*

3325	1	1992-1997	3⅝″	RA	£30-£35	$50-$60

Old Mr Bouncer™ Modeller David Lyttleton   *picture page 87*

2956	1	1986-1989	3″	Brown	£50-£75	$85-$125
2956	1	1989-1995	3″	RA	£30-£40	$50-$65

Shape No	Version	Production Period	Height	Backstamp	Market Value	

Old Mr Brown™ Modeller Albert Hallam   *picture page 87*

1796	1	1962-1971	3″	Gold	£75-£100	$125-$165
1796	1	1971-1989	3″	Brown	£40-£45	$65-$75
1796	1	1989-Cur	3″	RA	£16	

Old Mr Brown™ (character jug) Modeller Graham Tongue   *picture page 87*

| 2959 | 1 | 1987-1989 | 3″ | Brown | £100-£125 | $165-$205 |
| 2959 | 1 | 1989-1992 | 3″ | RA | £75-£100 | $125-$165 |

Old Mr Pricklepin™ Modeller David Lyttleon   *picture page 88*

| 2767 | 1 | 1983-1989 | 2½″ | Brown | £50-£75 | $85-$125 |
| 2767 | 1 | 1989 | 2½″ | RA | £350-£400 | $575-$660 |

Peter and the Red Pocket Handkerchief™
Modeller Martyn Alcock   *picture page 88*

| 3242 | 1 | 1991-Cur | 4¾″ | RA | £18 | |

Peter Ate A Radish™ Modeller Warren Platt   *picture page 88*

| 3533 | 1 | 1995-Cur | 4″ | RA | £18 | |

Peter in Bed™ Modeller Martyn Alcock   *picture page 89*

| 3473 | 1 | 1995-Cur | 2¾″ | RA | £18 | |

Peter Rabbit™ Modeller Arthur Gredington   *picture page 88*

1098	1	1947-1971	4½″	Gold	£70-£80	$115-$130
1098	1	1971-1983	4½″	Brown	£40-£50	$65-$85
1098	2	1983-1989	4½″	Brown	£30-£35	$50-$60
1098	2	1989-Cur	4½″	RA	£16	
1098[1]	2	1997	4½″	Bes	£25	

[1]Gold edition

Peter Rabbit™ Modeller Martyn Alcock   *picture page 88*

| 3356 | 3 | 1993-1997 | 6¾″ | RA | £30-£35 | $50-$60 |
| 3356[1] | 3 | 1997 | 6¾″ | Bes | £25 | |

[1]Gold edition – limited edition 1947

Peter Rabbit Gardening™ Modeller Warren Platt   *picture page 89*

| 3739 | 1 | 1998-cur | | New Bes | £16 | |

Peter Rabbit with Daffodils™ Modeller Amanda Hughes-Lubeck

| 3597 | 1 | 1996-cur | 4¾″ | RA | £20 | |

Shape No	Version	Production Period	Height	Backstamp	Market Value	

Peter Rabbit with Handkerchief™
Modeller Amanda Hughes-Lubeck   *picture page 89*

| 3592 | 1 | 1996-1997 | 7¼″ | RA | £40-£50 | $65-$85 |

Peter Rabbit with Postbag™ Modeller Amanda Hughes-Lubeck   *picture page 89*

| 3391 | 1 | 1996-cur | 4¾″ | RA | £20 | |

Peter Rabbit in a Gooseberry Net™ Modeller David Lyttleton   *picture page 88*

| 3157 | 1 | 1990-1995 | 2″ | RA | £40-£50 | $65-$85 |

Peter Rabbit™ (character jug) Modeller Graham Tongue   *picture page 89*

| 3006 | 1 | 1987-1989 | 3″ | Brown | £100-£125 | $165$205 |
| 3006 | 1 | 1989-1992 | 3″ | RA | £75-£100 | $125-$165 |

Peter Rabbit™ (plaque) Modeller Harry Sales & David Lyttleton

| 2650 | 1 | 1979-1982 | 7½″ | Brown | £60-£80 | $100-$130 |

Peter Rabbit™ (wall figural) Modeller Graham Tongue

| 2083 | 1 | 1967-1969 | 6″ | Gold | £1500-£2000 | $2475-$3300 |

Pickles™ Modeller Albert Hallam   *picture page 90*

| 2334 | 1 | 1971 only | 4½″ | Gold | £250-£300 | $415-$495 |
| 2334 | 1 | 1972-1982 | 4½″ | Brown | £200-£250 | $330-$415 |

Pig-Wig™ Modeller Albert Hallam   *picture page 90*

| 2381 | 1 | 1971 only | 4″ | Gold | £350-£400 | $575-$660 |
| 2381 | 1 | 1972-1982 | 4″ | Brown | £250-£300 | $415-$495 |

Pigling Bland™ Modeller Graham Orwell   *picture page 90*

1365	1	1955-1971	4¼″	Gold	£250-£300	$415-$495
1365	1	1972-1974	4¼″	Brown	£200-£250	$330-$415
1365	2	1974-1989	4¼″	Brown	£40-£50	$65-$85
1365	2	1989-1998	4¼″	RA	£30-£35	$50-$60

Pigling Eats His Porridge™ Modeller Martyn Alcock   *picture page 90*

| 3252 | 1 | 1991-1994 | 4″ | RA | £75-£100 | $125-$165 |

Poorly Peter Rabbit™ Modeller David Lyttleton   *picture page 90*

| 2560 | 1 | 1976-1989 | 3¾″ | Brown | £40-£50 | $65-$85 |
| 2560 | 1 | 1989-1997 | 3¾″ | RA | £30-£35 | $50-$60 |

Shape No	Version	Production Period	Height	Backstamp	Market Value	

Rebecca Puddle Duck™ Modeller David Lyttleton · *picture page 90*

Shape No	Version	Production Period	Height	Backstamp	Market Value	
2647	1	1981-1989	3¼″	Brown	£30-£35	$50-$60
2647	1	1989-Cur	3¼″	RA	£16	

Ribby™ Modeller Arthur Gredington · *picture page 91*

1199	1	1951-1971	3¼″	Gold	£75-£100	$125-$165
1199	1	1972-1989	3¼″	Brown	£30-£35	$50-$60
1199	1	1989-Cur	3¼″	RA	£16	

Ribby and the Patty Pan™ Modeller Martyn Alcock · *picture page 91*

3280	1	1992-Cur	3½″	RA	£16	

Sally Henny Penny™ Modeller Albert Hallam · *picture page 91*

2452	1	1973-1974	4″	Brown	£125-£150	$205-$250
2452	2	1974-1989	4″	Brown	£40-£50	$65-$85
2452	2	1989-1993	4″	RA	£30-£35	$50-$60

Samuel Whiskers™ Modeller Arthur Gredington · *picture page 91*

1106	1	1948-1971	3¾″	Gold	£100-£125	$165-$205
1106	1	1971-1989	3¾″	Brown	£50-£75	$85-$125
1106	1	1989-1995	3¾″	RA	£30-£40	$50-$65

Simpkin™ Modeller Alan Maslankowski · *picture page 91*

2508	1	1974-1982	4″	Brown	£300-£350	$495-$575

Sir Isaac Newton™ Modeller Graham Tongue · *picture page 92*

2425	1	1973-1984	3¾″	Brown	£250-£300	$415-$495

Squirrel Nutkin™ Modeller Arthur Gredington · *picture page 92*

1102	1	1948-1971	3¾″	Gold	£70-£80	$115-$130
1102	1	1971-1989	3¾″	Brown	£40-£50	$65-$85
1102	2	1989-Cur	3¾″	RA	£16	

Susan™ Modeller David Lyttleton · *picture page 92*

2716	1	1983-1989	4″	Brown	£125-£150	$205-$250
2716	1	1989	4″	RA	£350-£400	$575-$660

Tabitha Twitchit™ Modeller Arthur Greddington · *picture page 92*

1676	1	1960-1971	3½″	Gold	£125-£150	$205-$250
1676	1	1971-1974	3½″	Brown	£100-£125	$165-$205
1676	2	1974-1989	3½″	Brown	£40-£50	$65-$85
1676	2	1989-1995	3½″	RA	£30-£35	$50-$60

Shape No	Version	Production Period	Height	Backstamp	Market Value	

Tabitha Twitchit and Miss Moppet™ Modeller David Lyttleton   *picture page 93*

Shape No	Version	Production Period	Height	Backstamp	Market Value	
2544	1	1976-1989	3½"	Brown	£75-£100	$125-$165
2544	1	1989-1993	3½"	RA	£40-£50	$65-$85

Tailor of Gloucester™ Modeller Arthur Gredington   *picture page 93*

1108	1	1948-1971	3½"	Gold	£100-£125	$165-$205
1108	1	1971-1989	3½"	Brown	£75-£100	$125-$165
1108	1	1989-Cur	3½"	RA	£16	

Tailor of Gloucester™ Modeller Warren Platt   *picture page 93*

3449	1	1995-1997	7½"	RA	£30-£35	$50-$60

The Old Woman Who Lived In A Shoe™
Modeller Colin Melbourne   *picture page 93*

1545	1	1958-1971	2¾"	Gold	£70-£80	$115-$130
1545	1	1971-1989	2¾"	Brown	£40-£50	$65-$85
1545	1	1989-1997	2¾"	RA	£30-£35	$50-$60

The Old Woman Who Lived In A Shoe Knitting™
Modeller David Lyttleton   *picture page 94*

2804	1	1983-1989	3"	Brown	£100-£125	$165-$205
2804	1	1989-Cur	3"	RA	£16	

Thomasina Tittlemouse™ Modeller David Lyttleton   *picture page 94*

2668	1	1981-1989	3¼"	Brown	£50-£75	$85-$125
2668	1	1989	3¼"	RA	£350-£400	$575-$660

Timmy Tiptoes™ Modeller Arthur Gredington   *picture page 94*

1101	1	1948-1971	3¾"	Gold	£70-£80	$115-$130
1101	1	1971-1989	3¾"	Brown	£40-£50	$65-$85
1101	2	1989-1997	3½"	RA	£30-£35	$50-$60

Timmy Willie™ Modeller Arthur Gredington   *picture page 94*

1109	1	1948-1971	2½"	Gold	£70-£80	$115-$130
1109	1	1971-1989	2½"	Brown	£40-£50	$65-$85
1109	1	1989-1993	2½"	RA	£30-£35	$50-$60

Timmy Willie Sleeping™ Modeller Graham Tongue   *picture page 95*

2996	1	1987-1989	1¼"	Brown	£100-£125	$165-$205
2996	1	1989-1996	1¼"	RA	£40-£50	$65-$85

Shape No	Version	Production Period	Height	Backstamp	Market Value	

Tom Kitten™ Modeller Arthur Gredington   *picture page 95*

1100	1	1947-1971	3½″	Gold	£75-£100	$125-$165
1100	1	1971-1989	3½″	Brown	£40-£50	$65-$85
1100	2	1989-Cur	3½″	RA	£16	
1100[1]	2	1997	3½″	Bes	£25	

[1]Gold edition

Tom Kitten™ Modeller Martyn Alcock   *picture page 95*

| 3405 | 3 | 1994-1997 | 5¼″ | RA | £30-£35 | $50-$60 |

Tom Kitten in the Rockery™ Modeller Warren Platt   *picture page 96*

| 3719 | 13 | 1998-Cur | | New Bes | £16 | |

Tom Kitten Character Jug™ Modeller Ted Chawner   *picture page 95*

| 3103 | 1 | 1988-1989 | 3″ | Brown | £100-£125 | $165-$205 |
| 3103 | 1 | 1988-1992 | 3″ | RA | £75-£100 | $125-$165 |

Tom Kitten Plaque™ Modeller Graham Tongue   *picture page 96*

| 2085 | 1 | 1967-1969 | 6″ | Gold | £1500-£2000 | $2475-$3300 |

Tom Kitten and Butterfly™ Modeller Ted Chawner   *picture page 96*

| 3030 | 1 | 1987-1989 | 3½″ | Brown | £150-£200 | $250-$330 |
| 3030 | 1 | 1989-1994 | 3½″ | RA | £75-£100 | $125-$165 |

Tom Thumb™ Modeller Warren Platt   *picture page 96*

| 2989 | 1 | 1987-1989 | 3¼″ | Brown | £75-£100 | $125-$165 |
| 2989 | 1 | 1989-1997 | 3¼″ | RA | £30-£35 | $50-$60 |

Tommy Brock™ Modeller Graham Orwell   *picture page 96*

1348	1	1955-1971	3½″	Gold	£200-£250	$330-$415
1348	1	1971-1974	3½″	Gold	£175-£200	$290-$530
1348	2	1974-1989	3½″	Brown	£30-£35	$50-$60
1348	2	1989-Cur	3½″	RA	£16	

Tree Lamp Base™ Modeller James Hayward & Albert Hallam

| 1531 | 1 | 1958-1971 | 7″ | Gold | £150-£200 | $250-$330 |
| 1531 | 1 | 1971-1982 | 7″ | Brown | £125-£150 | $205-$250 |

NOTES

NOTES

NOTES

DALBRY ANTIQUES & COLLECTABLES

237 CANTERBURY ROAD
CANTERBURY VIC. 3126 AUSTRALIA

Tel (61 3) 98362301   Fax (61 3) 98886849   email dalbry@mira.net

Dear Collector,
We are delighted to be able to offer you this new addition to your Bunnykins collection, DB195, Sydney Bunnykins.

Sydney was commissioned by Dalbry Antiques & Collectables, in a special limited and numbered edition of 2500, with an exclusive backstamp for Dalbry. Sydney will be introduced in April 1999 and will be completed during the year 2000.

In designing Sydney, we aimed at producing an image, with an essentially Australian personality, expressing that bit of a larrikin present in lots of Aussies, with his rakishly tilted bush hat, the classic Stockmans shirt, the elastic sided boots and his moleskin trousers. With a wink in his eye, and a "thumbs up" approach to life, Sydney leans on a signpost directing all to his home town.

We now invite you to join us in welcoming Sydney to the Bunnykins world, and we hope you will enjoy Sydney as much as we do.

Brian Dalglish   Bill Bryant